SCIENCE AND RELIGION,

An Interpretation of Two Communities

by

HAROLD K. SCHILLING

CHARLES SCRIBNER'S SONS
New York

To Hulda

ACKNOWLEDGMENTS

The thesis of this book has grown gradually and with the help of many audiences in colleges and universities where I have lectured and conducted seminars, conferences and workshops on the subject. Because of their critical reactions and suggestions I have had to change my mind and modify my ideas many times. It will be obvious also that I have had the help of many writers whose books and articles I have read, and of many friends and colleagues with whom I have been able to discuss various aspects of the subject. Therefore I am deeply indebted to many people, many more than I could justify listing here.

Special acknowledgments with thanks are due the following: The Danforth Foundation supported five summer seminars, each two weeks in duration, at The Pennsylvania State University, for college and university teachers. For four of these I gave a series of daily lectures on science and religion. There was ample time for leisurely discussion, and I learned a great deal from these exchanges of views. During the annual meeting of the American Association for the Advancement of Science, December, 1955, I delivered an invited paper before the Philosophy of Science Section, which was later published in *Science* under the title of "A Human Enterprise." With the permission of the editor portions of this are reproduced here, with some modifications. In October of 1958, I delivered the George Walter Stewart Memorial Lecture at The State University of Iowa, entitled "Concerning the Nature of Science and Religion, A Study of Presuppositions." This was subsequently published by the University in pamphlet form. With the permission of the University I have reproduced a few paragraphs of this lecture in Chapter IX. In 1959, I collaborated with others in the preparation of a book entitled *Teacher Education and Religion,* published by the American Association of Colleges for Teacher Education. I prepared Chapter 5, "Teaching Reciprocal Relations Between Natural Science and Religion." A few passages from this are reproduced here with permission of the publishers.

While these projects forced me to start putting my ideas into writing, the impetus to finish the job came when I was invited to deliver six lectures at Oberlin College under the Mead-Swing Foundation in November of 1960. Part of the understanding was that I prepare the lectures in book form. Actually the manuscript that has emerged includes much more than could be included in the lectures. I am grateful to Oberlin for providing the occasion to prepare this book, and for the friendly interest the Mead-Swing Committee has shown in the matter. I am also thankful for the fact that at Oberlin one encounters critical and stimulating audiences. Since being there I have changed much of the manuscript because of questions posed and suggestions made by students and members of the faculty there.

Five persons have read my manuscript critically at various stages of its development—though none has seen the final version. They are Professors John Dillenberger and Gordon Harland, theologians and church historians at Drew University; Professor Edward LeRoy Long, Jr., of the Department of Religion at Oberlin College; Professor Ernest H. Freund of the Department of Philosophy, and Professor Rustum Roy, geochemist, both of The Pennsylvania State University. I am deeply indebted to them for frank, friendly and valuable suggestions.

James M. Gustafson has recently given us a book, *Treasure in Earthen Vessels, The Church as a Human Community* (Harper, 1961), to which I wish I could acknowledge indebtedness. Unfortunately it did not come to my attention until after mine went to press. All I can do now is to call attention to it and suggest that it is a remarkable, trailblazing book that should contribute greatly to our understanding of important but hitherto neglected communal aspects of the Church.

According to the enlightened policy of my University it is appropriate for "even a dean" to spend a part of his time in studies and in writing. For this opportunity and for aids, such as library and secretarial services, I am most grateful.

Acknowledgment with thanks is made of the help of two able secretaries, Mrs. Romaine Kaminski and Mrs. Bettye Dunsmore, whose interest and participation in the work seemed to me to be much more than duty alone called for.

Finally I am grateful for the permission of the Society for Promoting Christian Knowledge, London, to quote from its volume *Doctrine in The Church of England*.

HAROLD K. SCHILLING
The Pennsylvania State University

CONTENTS

CREEDS, ILLUSTRATIONS AND TABLES

CHAPTER I

Problem and Thesis

1 · THE SITUATION

The basic concern that has to a large extent motivated the writing of this book is not a new one with me. It came to a focus urgently in my thinking years ago, when I was a young instructor in college. I had bought a book, the title of which had caught my imagination. Though I did not know it at the time, its author, Alfred North Whitehead, was one of the really great sages of our time, and the book, *Science and the Modern World,* turned out to be one of his very best. One day while reading in it I came quite unexpectedly upon an assertion that struck me with terrific impact. Its implications were literally breath-taking. I have had to return to it many times, and it has influenced me tremendously. Here it is:

> When we consider what religion is for mankind and what science is, it is no exaggeration to say that the future course of history depends upon the decision of this generation as to the relations between them. We have here the two strongest general forces (apart from the mere impulse of the various senses) which influence men, and they seem to be set one against the other—the force of religious intuitions, and the force of our impulse to accurate observation and logical deduction.[1]

If the reader can appreciate why this should so profoundly affect a young scientist and teacher interested in the influence of his science upon youth, he will understand the basic purposes and goals of this book.

Whitehead is no longer with us. If he were, would his analysis of the situation today be the same? Probably it would. It is still true that among the forces that affect or shape our culture and our

1

individual lives, none are *more* influential than science and religion. Regardless of what our own personal attitudes toward them may be, each of us is conditioned by them to a large extent. Moreover, there can be no doubt that they are still widely regarded as opposed to each other, and this presents a serious problem—with ominous implications for the future.

The fact is that the world is in a state of boundless, abysmal confusion and disruptive tension, and that many of our individual lives are also. If we are to resolve the complex issues that threaten to disintegrate both our culture and our personal selves, we shall need to make use of all our resources. But if two such potent resources as science and religion seem to be in opposition, they in effect cancel each other out, and thus both become unavailable. Therefore, we must individually and collectively look at this situation candidly, settle once and for all whether they are irreconcilable in fact and by necessity, or not, and then decide what to do about it. And we urgently need to do this now.

Now in what sense do science and religion seem to be opposed today? The old warfare between them has largely disappeared. For most of us "creation versus evolution" is no longer an issue; nor is the question of the age or the shape of the earth, or of the structure of the heavens. Many thinking persons in one way or another have resolved problems like that of miracles. Much of the Church, certainly as it is represented by its best minds, recognizes and takes into account all that is significant in modern science. I am aware of no established scientific discovery or conclusion which it rejects or proscribes; and there are many that it has appropriated for the clarification of its own understanding. And yet for many people science and religion seem utterly opposed, or at least incompatible. Why?

The difficulty is complex and not easily analyzed. One can, however, recognize two general types of perplexity, first those that represent substantive disagreement, and second, those involving apparently incompatible or antagonistic attitudes. The former are characterized by the clash of contradictory teachings. Virtually all of the old issues of the warfare between science and religion were of this type. About these it should be remarked that they appear for the most part in those areas of inquiry, and at such times, when exploratory work is still going on and when conclusions have not yet been established, that is when new controversial ideas are still in their nascent state of development.

As we shall see later there are in general two phases or stages in the development of concepts and doctrines. One is the pioneering stage, and the other that of colonization or consolidation. It is during the former, when observation and fact finding are still far from complete and when overarching and integrating theoretical structures are still in the process of formation, that most controversies occur. It is, however, in the latter, after insights have been more completely clarified, new knowledge has become established and when things are seen in wider and deeper perspectives, that the controversial issues disappear. This is why we can say today that the old warfare has largely disappeared. It is because the old issues have been resolved, since we have passed beyond the frontier stage and have more complete knowledge and more encompassing understandings, in the light of which what formerly seemed contradictory now seems thoroughly harmonious and consistent.

Today there are new issues; but it is not difficult to see that these too are of the kind that are characteristic of the frontiers of knowledge. In the old controversies religious thought was confronted by the new conceptions of the physical and biological sciences. But these no longer present serious problems of the first kind. Today the focus of difficulty is in the social sciences. But I have no doubt that when these sciences have progressed somewhat farther beyond their frontier stages, and when religious thought has developed correspondingly in the growth of its own ideas and of its understanding of the social sciences, present controversies between them will also disappear.

Actually, as I see it, there are today but few problems of the first kind. For the most part for *our* generation it is not so much a question of specific contradictory teachings as of what seem to be incongruous attitudes and feelings, and conflicting purposes and goals. In large part these latter difficulties seem to me to arise from widespread misunderstandings as to the actual nature of science and religion, of their basic objectives and the methods they employ to achieve these, of their attitudes toward truth and freedom of inquiry, and toward the needs of mankind. Both science and religion are commonly thought of largely in terms of stereotypes that misrepresent their real nature. Many of the ideas and attitudes attributed to them have either never existed or been discarded long ago. It is often said that this is an "age of science," but surely, this is true only in a qualified sense. To be sure, it is an age in which science has greatly affected our physical environment and way of life as well as our conceptions of the universe. But it is not an age in which the nature and genius of science itself are widely understood or appreciated. Professor Herbert Dingle of the University of London, distinguished astrophysicist, as well as philosopher and historian of science, has said: "When we contemplate the ideas of the essential nature of science which are prevalent and operative today we find a situation fit to make the angels weep." [2] Nor is it an age in which the spirit of science has become dominant, i.e., in which science is valued more for the truth it reveals than for the gadgetry it provides, and in which its ideals of freedom of inquiry and expression, and of the primacy of evidence and reason, have been commonly accepted.

Similarly, this is not an age in which religion is widely understood, or its ideals accepted widely in practice. It, too, is thought of largely in terms of unfortunate stereotypes. Certainly this is true of Christianity, to which there are attributed cosmological and theological ideas and ecclesiastical practices that do not properly represent it today. Recently a renowned Scottish theologian, the late John Baillie, noted this fact in a series of lectures on "Why I Am a Christian." In his introduction he referred to the well known essay by Bertrand Russell on *Why I Am Not a Christian,* and remarked that if to be a Christian meant what Lord Russell seemed to think it meant, he, John Baillie, would not want to be a Christian either.

It is largely to these stereotyped images of religion and science that I ascribe the widespread notion that they must be basically incompatible or even inimical. Let me illustrate. Religion is said to have rigid creeds to which one *must* subscribe, whereas science does not. Religion is allegedly authoritarian, demanding unquestioning orthodoxy, whereas science is utterly free, recognizing neither orthodoxy nor heresy. We are told that the authority of religion stems fundamentally from so-called "revelation," a mysterious process by which God is said to have transmitted historical, scientific and religious knowledge, contained in an inerrant Bible, that is unattainable by ordinary rational means, while that of science is based on evidence and reason, without appeal to anything as meaningless as "revelation." In religion one must take things by unquestioning faith in spite of the absence of proof; whereas in science one rejects everything not based on logical demonstration and experimental verification.

No wonder science and religion seem mutually exclusive! No wonder many thoughtful people feel that it would be intellectually dishonest if one adhered to both. Note, however, that the issues here pertain not so much to clashes of particular teachings of competing substantive beliefs, as to alleged incompatibility of attitudes and ideals, of basic method and general point of view.

There is another aspect of the matter of attitudes. Not only has there seemed to be opposition between the forces of science and religion, but there has been developing a feeling that they are mutually irrelevant to each other, intellectually and otherwise, and that they would both be better off if they paid no attention to each other. Of what good is religion in the pursuit of science? What positive contribution can it make to the growth of science? Perhaps we have come to the point in history where religion is no longer an active opponent of science or a positive hindrance to scientific progress, but is it not still likely to be a dead weight causing retardation, or a siphon drawing off the interests and energies of men from what is really important and urgent in the life of the world? And of what good is science to religion? What contribution has it made or can it make to the solution of religious problems—in view of its preoccupation with things and its amoral attitude toward values? May it not actually be a millstone around the neck of spiritual progress?

Thus it must be said about both science and religion that many representatives of each regard the other as banal and pointless, and even possibly harmful, in regard to what really matters in life and in scholarship. Nor is this feeling to be found only within the camps of science and religion themselves. On the one hand, as Edmund Husserl [3] pointed out rather cogently, in referring to what he called "the crisis of the European sciences," the common man has for some time been asking rather dispairingly what the sciences have to offer aside from materialistic values in these times of great perplexity and anxiety. For many men and women they seem to have no answers to the questions that concern man most deeply. On the other hand, the same charges are being made against the religions of the world. What are they doing for us in our time of trouble? Referring more specifically to the Christian Church as the common man often sees it—and the intellectual as well—the questions it asks and speaks to seem in the main to be of interest only to its own ecclesiastical self. Nobody else is asking them—so it is said. And on the ones to which humanity does cry out for answers it is strangely mute—either oblivious or helpless. What all this means is that science and religion do not only seem irrelevant to each other, but the opinion of each with respect to the other is shared by large segments of mankind that regard both as being utterly inconsequential when judged in terms of genuinely humane values and concerns.

2 · THE THESIS

Now, to me, such views as to the nature of science and religion seem tragically unfortunate. In the first place, they grossly misrepresent the basic facts about both. At their best they simply are not like that. In the second place, as long as these clichés prevail in the public mind they create psychological blocks that effectively frustrate any attempts truly to understand science and religion, and to relate them constructively. It is my purpose to present an alternative interpretation of them, one that seems to me to correspond more accurately to the facts of the case.

My thesis is that they are fundamentally not incompatible and inimical, and that they are not irrelevant either to each other or to the greatest concerns and needs of mankind. They are, of course, different in many respects, but not in such a way as to make them necessarily opposed or mutually irrelevant. Indeed in other ways they are remarkably alike—especially in those very aspects in which they are typically regarded as most incongruous, namely in their spirit, temper of mind, and in their basic attitude toward truth and reason, and freedom of inquiry, as well as toward the spiritual, non-material necessities of life. I shall argue that such differences as do exist, far from making them discordant or mutually exclusive, make them complementary and mutually helpful and beneficial. Each is unique and each has something unique to offer. Each is enriched by the other. Neither need be a hindrance to the other. We need them both in our culture and our personal lives. Our world view and philosophy of life would be incomplete and unbalanced without the contributions of both.

This book has then a rather modest purpose, namely to help develop an atmosphere of informed, mutual understanding and appreciation within which the difficult task of relating science and religion meaningfully can be undertaken, in which the insights and methods of each can more effectively enrich the other, and in which they can together contribute more significantly to the attainment of a well balanced life and world view.

In what follows the term science will refer for the most part to the natural rather than the social sciences. In part this is because I know much less about the latter. In part, however, it is also because, as I have hinted earlier, the social sciences seem not to have advanced as far beyond the earlier frontier stages of their development and it is therefore much more difficult to discern what their characteristic methods and attitudes are, either internally or *vis-à-vis* religion. I suspect, moreover, that the attitudinal problems we are to consider are essentially the same for all the sciences and can therefore be portrayed and analyzed quite adequately even though the study focuses much more on the physical sciences. I hope, therefore, that my remarks will not seem altogether inapplicable to the social sciences. For similar, though not identical, reasons the term religion will refer in the main to the Judaeo-Christian tradition, and probably more often than not to Protestant Christianity. Here too I hope that the point of view presented will not seem inappropriate with respect to other faiths.

I shall not provide a specific definition of either science or religion. They are so comprehensive and many-sided that no brief definitions of them can possibly be adequate, and that their meanings can therefore be conveyed only contextually.

It should be understood, however, that quite frankly it is my purpose to describe and interpret them at their best and loftiest

—as I see them. One way to cause misunderstanding and conflict between two persons, or nations, or ideologies—and certainly between science and religion—is to portray them in terms of their least desirable qualities and manifestations. Another is to point out what is best in one and worst in the other and then compare these. I shall try to avoid both these errors.

The interpretation is governed by three basic principles, among others. First it must be factual, i.e., truthfully descriptive. As we shall see, however, significant statements of fact always have an interpretive component. So-called facts are never "seen" except in a perspective that reveals them in relationship to other facts or to existing conceptual structures. Always a fact, or a group of them, is viewed through an interpretive screen of some sort. It is, of course, possible—if not actually necessary—in attempting a factual analysis or description to choose among several alternative interpretive screens.

This then brings us to the second principle. There are in our culture today many centrifugal forces and tendencies threatening to disrupt and tear it apart. Among these are certain ways of looking at things that tend to shatter the unity of scholarship and thought, and among people to cause estrangement and antagonism, suspicion and fear. Without at this time referring to any of these in particular, I suggest that it is a sound principle of scholarship whenever possible—and consistent with truth—to invoke those modes of thought and interpretations that are centripetal and cohesive in their tendencies and effects, that tend to hold things together. In science a good theory is one that unifies in one conceptual structure as much empirical knowledge as possible. There, when one is confronted by two alternative theories, one that leaves two groups of facts in apparent isolation or incongruity, and one that unifies them in apparent harmony, it is the second that is to be preferred. The same criterion of desirability applies when one must choose between two interpretations in other fields.

And last, it is intended that this interpretation shall be descriptive in the sense of being confessional, to use a term made so meaningful by H. Richard Niebuhr,[4] rather than argumentative or defensive. Accordingly then my stance will be that of a witness endeavoring to give testimony regarding what he knows from his participation in the life and thought of science and religion, and especially in his case Christianity. I shall not be an advocate grinding an ax for any particular brand of philosophy or theology, or attempting to *prove* or *disprove* any particular doctrine of science or religion. Where I must make interpretive choices it will be in the spirit, and in the interest of centripetal unification rather than centrifugal fragmentation and separation. Moreover, I shall for the most part be concerned with depicting them at their best *as they are today*. In so far as I shall speak of their past I shall do this from the viewpoint of present insights. This is legitimate because each has an impressive history of growth and development, and a continuous tradition, and because just as the present can be understood adequately only in terms of the past, so the past becomes truly meaningful only as seen through the present.

3 · HOW THE THESIS IS DEVELOPED

This section is presented as a brief abstract of the book. Some readers may prefer to read it as a preview before proceeding, and others may want to come back to it for a summary of what they have read. Its reading is not basic to an understanding of what follows.

The next chapter endeavors to clarify in broad terms what science and religion are in their essentials and in their various modalities, and how they may be distinguished in regard to the basic questions they ask, the fundamental concerns that motivate them, and the character of the conceptual content of their thought and teachings. Fundamental concepts that will appear in the course of this comparative study are *nature, God, ultimate* and *preliminary concerns, I-and-Thou, I-and-It, faith,* and *belief*. Using these, religion—especially Christianity—may be characterized as a faith relationship to God, the God beyond the gods, beyond even the God of theism. It is a deeply personal I-and-Thou relationship, out of which come questions and answers of ultimate concern, and that eventuates in love of and service for mankind. Faith here is not a *believing that,* but a *believing in,* a trusting, self-committing state of being, an orientation of life and thought. It is not a credulous subscribing to prescribed doctrine. On the other hand, belief *is* a believing that something is true. Science, by contrast, is a faith relationship to nature. It is much less personal, an I-and-It relationship, out of which come questions of more preliminary concern. The beliefs of science are about nature, while those of religion are about God, and especially God in relation to man and the world. While science and religion may be regarded as *logically* separate, they do touch *existentially* in many actual situations and concerns of life.

In the third chapter certain prevailing stereotypes are studied in the attempt to show what science and religion are not. Thus science is not what is usually implied for it by the stereotype of "the scientific method," namely an essentially automatic machine for attaining truth by taking certain prescribed "steps" and employing inerrant logic and precise definitions. It is here that we differentiate between science of the frontier and of the hinterland, and find that "the scientific method" as it is commonly understood does not exist, and that science has many methods rather than one. Similarly, religion is not what the stereotype of "divine revelation" ordinarily implies for it, i.e., a way by which religious truth comes to man inerrantly by divine dictation. According to dominant contemporary theological conceptions, revelation is fundamentally not propositional, a direct disclosure of truth, but an opening of heart and mind, an enlarged and sensitized awareness that makes possible God's self-disclosure, especially through events and acts in history.

An exceedingly fruitful way of characterizing both science and religion is to think of them as human and social enterprises, in which goals and purposes are achieved only through sharing and mutual understanding and support. Basically they are not solitary in nature, but communal, and their insights come out of common rather than private life, work and thought. Some of the more significant implications of this, including those about the institutional aspects of science and religion, are explored in Chapter IV. Not a few seemingly paradoxical aspects of the life and history of the Church become meaningful in the light of this key concept of community.

This is then followed, in Chapter V, by an analysis of the basic typical interests and activities of the two communities. Their work and thought have three main components, namely the empirical, the theoretical and the transformative. These are, of course, related closely, and in practice they always overlap to some extent and interact dynamically; and yet they are recognizably different in purpose and method. There are two special emphases in this chapter, namely upon the exposition and clarification of the meaning and role of "experience" and of "theory," and their interrelations in both science and religion. In this way the often suspect enterprise of theology is seen to have very important functions and be an inevitable and necessary part of religion, just as theory is in science. Another concept that makes its appearance here is "circularity." Science and religion are *circular* in that essentially they are non-logical in character, in the sense that their three main components are so interdependent that each one of them depends upon the other two, and yet none is the necessary logical foundation of any of the others.

The question arises then, in Chapters VI and VII, devoted respectively to science and religion, whether so non-logical a threefold and circular process can and does yield *knowledge* and *insight* that are characterized by *permanence* and *certainty*. The answer of each of the communities is yes. In the history of each there has been a growing accumulation of insight that has remained permanent, that succeeding generations have accepted as reliable and certain, in contrast to other elements of communal insight that have been transient. Lists of permanent and transient beliefs are presented to illustrate this. Analysis of such permanent and transient items indicates that these are identifiable respectively, as a first approximation, with the experiential-factual findings and the theoretical-interpretive conceptual structures of science and religion. Moreover, in both, what is regarded as *certain* and *permanent* is regarded as also *true,* as that term is used in common-sense realism. It seems then that truth-claims should be made for statements of what has been experienced, but not for statements of theoretical (theological) explanation.

In the second of these chapters, the seventh, the subject of religious creeds and creedal language is considered at some length, together with such related matters as their basic intent and message, their alleged rigidity, their relation to revelation, and the dogmatism that has been associated with them. In this connection, finally, there is a study of corresponding creedal phenomena in science.

Clearly the subject we have been working up to is that of cognition and knowledge. It now becomes the main subject of the next three chapters, the eighth, ninth and tenth, in which more specifically we discuss *concepts,* their meanings, their methodological and cultural origins and functions, their role with regard to fact and theory, and their interrelations and interactions. Concepts have in general more than one meaning or component of meaning; most have two and some three. Certain important three-valued concepts are studied in detail, e.g., "light" from physics and "God" from religious thought. They are seen to have meanings arising from three components of the cognitive process: experience and empirical analysis, intuition and inherited presuppositions, and mental construction and postulation. Corresponding to these are three kinds of verification and validation.

Out of this analysis emerges the idea of a continuous spectrum of cognition and knowledge, extending from the physical sciences, through biological and social sciences, through the arts to religion. It is proposed that some characteristics of knowledge and of the cognitive process vary continuously within the spectrum from one end to the other, but that others remain constant. Thus we can speak of "knowledge" in all these fields and assert that in an important sense the way it is attained is the same for all of them. There is therefore no discontinuous separation of science and religion as far as cognition is concerned.

In the tenth chapter there is also an extensive discussion of the three-way conceptual interactions and influences among the sciences, religions and the cultures surrounding them, and of the related subject of presuppositions. Not only are there such interactions in the conceptual realm, but also in that of faith and myth. This is taken up in Chapter XI. The question is asked: Whither mankind? and it is considered in terms first of more immediate concerns and then of more ultimate ones. In this connection science and religion are seen to be today sources of both hope and despair. Two great myths are identified as being dominant in the West, the new scientific myth of Evolution and the old Judaeo-

Christian myth. Can they or may they be interpreted as coming out of and expressing two inevitably competitive faiths, or as in essence one?

The last problem dealt with from the viewpoint of the light it can shed upon the nature of science and religion is that of religious pluralism and relativism—in the last chapter.

As this thesis and the method underlying it have evolved and been presented at different stages of development to various audiences, some commentators have described them as an attempt to explore and exploit analogies between science and religion and to build up an argument by analogy. This I have never been able to understand, since that has certainly not been my intention. To be sure, in the course of the investigation I have been surprised to discover certain similarities and differences between science and religion of which I was formerly totally unaware, and I have come to feel that the explicit recognition and understanding of these contributes much to the clarification of the nature of both science and religion. I would plead, however, that what I am presenting here are the results of a factual comparative study that has not been a playing with analogies, but a search for actualities.

It should be noted that no attempt is made herein to solve the problems arising out of the various relationships of science and religion to each other. There are many such problems, but discussion of them with a view to their solution does not belong in this book. Solutions may seem to be implied or foreshadowed by this study. It may even be that some of the "problems" will evaporate and therefore be seen not to need "solution" as the nature of science and of religion become better understood. But all that I have attempted here is to contribute to such more adequate understanding and thus to help prepare the stage for informed and fruitful discussion that may lead to solutions.

CHAPTER II

What Science and Religion Are

How to Distinguish Them

1 · PROBLEMS OF DEFINITION

What do we mean by *science* and *religion,* and how may they be differentiated? How can or should such a question be answered, i.e., what criteria should an answer meet if it is to be satisfactory? This latter question is especially important for our purposes because many definitions and conceptions current today are not in my opinion satisfactory—especially those that are too narrow. Thus science is often identified simply with the sum total of its subject matter content, the aggregate of its ideas, laws, principles and theories—nothing more. As a distinguished physicist once said, "Physics is what can be expressed by its partial differential equations. Everything else is external to it." This seems quite inadequate to me, and so do similarly restricted conceptions of religion.

The business of defining anything, or giving it a name and saying what we mean by it, is of course to some extent arbitrary. But it is by no means *only* arbitrary, for there are important matters of fact as well as of strategy to be taken into account. As to factual matters, we should ask what meanings are actually current in common usage. Does a proposed definition adequately depict *all* the important features of that which is being defined? As to strategy, which one of a variety of usages might help us to see most clearly how the defined fits into the whole scheme of things, what its true significance, value and implications are for thought and life, what people do with it, and what it does to them?

Applying these criteria as we look first at science, it must be realized that for many scientists, science is something big, many-sided

14

and far-reaching, rich with significance and potent in influence—
and much more than its specific intellectual content. That this is
recognized widely also among non-scientists is indicated by the
fact that the term *science* has a variety of common usages. To be
sure, science *is* a body of organized knowledge that may, as in
the case of physics, be exhibited by an array of equations. But
this is only one usage. Science is spoken of also—and I think
with equal propriety—as a way or method of knowing. From another point of view it is an area of experience—experience with
nature, and experience in creativity. Still another and a somewhat
more inclusive common usage is that of a certain attitude, point
of view, or even, in a rich sense, a way of life. Surely this is the
meaning conveyed when it is said that science is openminded,
tolerant, and given to the unfettered quest for truth for its own
sake. In still another shade of meaning, science is often spoken
of as a potent force or influence for good in the world—and quite
properly so. Look at what it has done technologically, and even
more, what it has done spiritually, in fighting *against* superstition
and ignorance, and *for* freedom of inquiry, critical thinking, and
for the experimental approach in the attack upon problems. Moreover, science is an actual social enterprise, an undertaking, an historical movement.

There are those who urge that it is meaningless to say that
science *does* anything, or that it asserts this and denies that. We
are told that to speak thus is to be guilty of unjustifiable personifi-
cation. After all, they say, science is not a metaphysical entity that
exists and acts. The fact is that many people—and very intelligent ones too—do speak that way, and that it conveys important
meaning. The reason why it does, and why, moreover, science *is*
spoken of in a variety of ways, is that it actually has many aspects
and exists in a variety of modes.[1] Unless, when we are trying to
say what science is, we employ all of these usages we shall not
be able to tell the whole story about it—and its nature. Furthermore, everybody should know that no one thinks of science as a
metaphysical entity or objective reality, and that linguistic per-
sonification does not necessarily imply it.

Similar remarks apply also to religion. It, too, can be defined
narrowly in terms of only its internal content of ideas and practices.

But surely it is in fact much more than that. Like science it is in part an organized body of insight, *and* an area of experience, *and* a way of knowing, *and* a way of thinking, *and* a point of view or orientation, *and* a way of life. Undeniably it is an influence in the world. It too has fought superstition and ignorance, authoritarianism and so on. It, likewise, is a social enterprise, and an active, vital and dynamic component of our culture. Religion simply is not understood unless it is known and defined in all of these ways.

So much, then, for the facts of the case that have a bearing upon the business of definition and the clarification of meaning. Now let us look at the strategic aspects of it. I submit that the use of definitions or understandings that are too narrow is stultifying, impedes thought and progress. Nowhere is this more evident than in the field of "science and religion." Here even Paul Tillich seems to me to be making a mistake by thinking of science—and religion for that matter—in too restricted a sense. Of recent years he has said repeatedly (or has repeatedly been reported as saying) that science and religion are so utterly different that they do not and cannot touch in such a way as to come into either conflict or accord, and that therefore neither can say anything that would either discredit or credit the other. He asserts that they come into contact only indirectly through their philosophical implications. Karl Barth seems to me to take an even more extreme separatist or exclusivist position.

Of course, their general point of view has much to commend it. As we shall see, science and religion do have radically different concerns and therefore ask utterly different questions. We do not go to church or consult the priest professionally if we want to learn about the properties of gases or electrons or protozoa. Nor do we go to the research laboratory or consult the scientist professionally in order to learn about the ultimate meaning of worship and prayer, or whether Jesus was the Christ, or whether God is present and active in history. Never again should theologians "butt in" to declare a scientific theory or empirical finding to be untenable on theological grounds. Never again should scientists "butt in" to declare theological theories and religious experience to be untenable on purely scientific grounds. Both kinds of inter-

HSBC

vention are indefensible logically. In this important sense science and religion must indeed be conceived narrowly and be kept apart. Each has its own area of competence which the other must respect and not violate.

To stop there, however, is to adopt a sterile or even harmful approach. It solves no real problems. It only sidesteps them on jurisdictional grounds. What is more, it misrepresents the actual existential situation. It does not follow that because science and religion are separate "logically" they do not—or should not—touch and interact in other ways.

Every teacher who knows students as well as science, and every pastor who knows people as well as theology, knows that science and religion do touch and interact in people's minds and hearts. Sometimes indeed this is a matter of formal reasoning in the upper reaches of philosophical implication, but sometimes it is not. Often people feel it in their bones that their religious views cannot remain unaffected by progress in scientific thought, and that the enterprise of science must not be exempt from scrutiny and criticism stemming from religious concerns. More often than not this is a subconscious interaction, a visceral rather than cerebral kind of thinking. This is so because science and religion have become for them much more than particular, circumscribed, delimited bodies of ideas. Let me illustrate.

In contemporary physics we emphasize the importance of operational definitions and descriptions. Whenever possible we try to explain what we mean by references to what happens, and to what we do, in laboratory or field. Consider then the case of a student who has been acclimated in contemporary physics to the extent that he engages *habitually* in such operational thinking. When asked, for instance, what is meant by the statement, "A sodium flame is yellow," he immediately, i.e., without deliberate premeditation, replies by describing how *sodium* and *flame,* and *yellow* may be identified in the laboratory by means of certain operations. When confronted by metaphysical definitions, in terms of metaphysical properties and abstractions and purely mental constructs, he is uncomfortable. Knowledge to him represents, then, something definable operationally. Suppose now that he reads the statement, "I know that my redeemer liveth." His immediate reaction to this, and the question he will ask automatically, will not stem from a conscious desire for logical or linguistic analysis—indeed may not represent deliberate, conscious thought at all, but rather a visceral, subconscious demand. If he goes to his pastor or teacher for clarification his immediate need is, whether he realizes it or not, for some sort of "operational" or experiential explication, not a discourse on metaphysical entities or beings. He may be intellectually mature enough to be interested in the latter also, but if so, this is likely to come later. In this case, then, science and religion (defined broadly) have indeed touched and interacted dynamically—existentially, sub-logically, and sub-philosophically. This, incidentally, is why it is important to explore the attitudinal interrelations of science and religion, as distinguished from the logical ones.

Another example. One of the first things many science teachers do in a beginning course is to demonstrate illusions, to show how fallible our sense perceptions are. We have all seen how easy it is to draw wrong conclusions optically, e.g., that straight lines appear curved under some circumstances; and how difficult it is by the sense of touch to decide whether one sample of water is warmer or cooler than another; and to judge by muscular tension which one of two bodies weighs more than the other. After illustrating this the science teacher then demonstrates how much easier it is to make such decisions with the help of measuring instruments. As the student's laboratory experience grows, he develops a pronounced suspicion of purely subjective judgments and tremendous respect for the so-called objective methods of science. Now imagine his immediate reaction when confronted by the statement of Job's, the one in which he addresses God as follows: "I have uttered what I did not understand, things too wonderful for me, which I did not know. . . . I had heard of Thee by the hearing of the ear, but now my eye sees Thee." It will not be a sign of cynical skepticism on his part if he asks: Does this mean anything? Didn't Job simply experience an illusion or hallucination? Nor would such questions necessarily indicate philosophic sophistication, for the student's reaction might well be more visceral than cerebral, if I may put it that way again.

One more illustration of how science and religion do in fact

interact, this time an even more obvious case of sublogical conflict. I refer to the infamous Nazi biological and psychological experiments with prisoners and Jews during the war. Now from the
point of view of a narrowly defined science, one that is interested
only in gaining "knowledge," such experiments are not only
justifiable but desirable. How else can one discover when death
occurs as one reduces the temperature of the body over a wide
range, or increases the intensity of electric or chemical shock
treatment, than by deliberately crossing the threshold values of
death and actually killing people? Moreover, how can one establish
the threshold values accurately, except by deliberately repeating
the experiment, and actually killing many times so as to reduce the
probable error to a desired magnitude? What is scientifically wrong
about deliberately driving a baby—or many babies—crazy in order that we may know more about the conditions that produce
insanity, and what it means to be, or become, crazy, and what the
various characteristics of insanity are at an early age? From a purely
scientific point of view, nothing whatsoever. Think of how much
more rapidly science would advance, and how our knowledge of
death, insanity, pain, disease, hatred and stupidity would grow, if
we induced these states in people at will and then experimented
with them under control conditions.

And yet consider the widespread profound horror and revulsion
at this sort of thing. Clearly this is a religious reaction—deriving
from ultimate concerns, from the sense of the sanctity of human
life, or in many cases from a sense of responsibility to God and
therefore to man as child of God. Here science and religion do
touch on a profound issue, in a clashing of basic purposes and
values. It should be said, of course, that much more often they
touch in a mood of mutual interest and re-enforcement of purpose
and determination, witness their common attack upon ignorance,
disease and hunger, as well as other disabilities and evils.

Now we must remind ourselves that we entered upon this discussion not for the purpose of explicitly identifying and considering such existential contacts and interactions, but in order to shed
light upon the nature of science, as well as of religion, and upon
the problem of saying what we mean by them. I have tried to
make two points. First, too narrow a definition of either science

or religion misrepresents the facts, and gives too restricted a picture of what it means in the world. Second, to do so is strategically bad, because it hampers our efforts to relate science and religion meaningfully, by creating the impression that they are utterly separate, whereas in fact they do interact in a variety of ways. For both these reasons, then, I shall present descriptive sketches rather than formal definitions in attempting to say what they are and are not.

2 · THE QUESTIONS THEY ASK

One way to depict the nature of science and religion is to point out their basic concerns and the questions they ask, and to show how they may be distinguished in this respect.

The sciences ask such questions as the following: What is the chemical composition of this object? How long, or heavy, or soft, or magnetic is it? How does that machine work? By what sequence does one event follow or depend upon another? How can a particular train of events be initiated, controlled and stopped? What theories can be constructed to correlate in simple fashion various particular bodies of data and of natural law for explanatory or predictive purposes? The concern here is for information; information about matter and energy in its many forms, biological phenomena and processes, psychological behavior and social structures—all within the dimensions of space, time and mass. It is a seeking also of broad principles or patterns of thought by which relationships in nature may be "seen" and employed for various purposes.

The questions asked in religion are very different. There we ask: Why? Whence? Whither? What does it mean? Who am I? Who are you? What should we be like? What is life and what is its meaning? What is death, and why? How is my destiny determined? By myself? By nature? By chance? By other determiners, perhaps beyond the sensually perceptible and otherwise empirically knowable? Whatever they may be, how should I relate myself to them in order that I may truly live and worthily die?

It is evident that such questions call for much more than scientific information. They reach out toward the realm of wonder, of inscrutable mystery, the ultimate beyond, and point toward the ground of our being, the source of confidence and hope. They are the kind of questions that appear when at times of reflection the mind reaches out to get beyond itself and its visible environment, when it becomes aware of spiritual significance and reality, and of corresponding responsibilities and opportunities, when it becomes conscious of the ethical and moral aspect of life and of its import. They seem to take on tremendous, urgent importance especially in times of crisis or of special significance, such as birth, death, falling in love, marriage, divorce, suffering, great achievement or dismal failure, or shattering anxiety.

To put it another way, while the sciences ask about the natural and social phenomena and events themselves, religion asks about their ultimate meaning. While the sciences confine their inquiry within the dimensions of space, time and mass, religion extends its concern into the realm having the additional dimension of "depth," where man encounters purpose and ethical demands, and the phenomena of holiness and unholiness, righteousness and sin, salvation and doom.

3 · PERSONAL CONCERNS

Not only do science and religion differ, however, in the kinds of questions they ask, but in the urgency and "concern" that impel the asking, and in the existential * importance that is imputed to both the questions and answers. Paul Tillich has given us an exceedingly fruitful and clarifying conception of religion by proposing that it is "ultimate concern," as contrasted with the concerns of the sciences and the common, ordinary concerns of everyday life that he regards as more immediate and "preliminary." Religion has to do then with what matters most to us and affects our entire being. Tillich has explained that *"ultimate* concern" is concern that springs from loving God with all of one's heart, soul, mind and strength, and one's neighbor as oneself.

Religion is then a state of deep personal whole involvement and commitment, since there can be no ultimate concern without such

---

* As I use the term "existential" it relates to personal existence and deeply personal significance.

unreserved involvement. Contrary to popular opinion, there is personal involvement in science too, as I shall try to show later. But this is not by any means complete involvement of all of one's self, since there one endeavors to disregard personal concerns and involvements as much as possible. This is one meaning of the term "to be objective."

Still another way of characterizing this particular difference between science and religion is to employ the tremendously meaningful ideas developed by Martin Buber,[2] namely those of "I-and-Thou" and "I-and-It." The deep significance suggested by the expression "I and Thou" is not nearly as evident in English as in the German idiom *Ich und Du*. The German *Du,* of which *Thou* is the English translation, is used by Germans only in conversation between intimates, very close friends, or lovers, and members of one's own family, in contrast to the formal *Sie,* used when addressing a mere acquaintance or stranger. In choosing *Ich und Du,* rather than *Ich und Sie* (*I and Thou* rather than *I and You*) Buber wished to symbolize an intensely personal relationship that characterizes religion, one presupposing real community of interest, of deep mutual understanding, confidence and trust, between two beings having genuine solicitude and love for each other. Science, on the other hand, progresses by the increase of knowledge gained in I-and-It relationships and encounters. Here a subject *I* confronts an object impersonally as an *It,* even though that "object" may itself be personal, and imposes upon it critical, analytic scrutiny, manipulation and control.

4 · NATURE AND GOD

One may say also that science centers its attention upon *that* which is symbolized by the word "nature," while religion focuses upon *that* symbolized by the term "God." These terms represent two of the most remarkable integrating, revelatory insights that have appeared in the history of ideas. Many a tome has been written about each, and I shall not now expound them more than to indicate how they help us to see an essential difference between science and religion.

Nature means to most scientists, I think, the whole economy or

system of observable phenomena and things, including man, existing in time and space, and held together in a field or web of cause-
and-effect relationships. It took a long time to develop this idea.
Apparently the concept of "nature," as we think of it, did not
exist among the Hebrews. Nowhere do we encounter in the Bible
such language as *"mother nature,"* or *"nature does this or that."*
Nor is the idea of *natural law* biblical; it is post-biblical. The biblical idea that seems to come closest to the concept of nature is
creation, as in "all creation groaneth."

Both the Hebrew and the early Christian interpreted the regu-
larities of the astronomical heavens, and the sequence of the
seasons and of seed-to-plant-to-seed, not in terms of a cause-and-
effect system, but of a direct moment-by-moment action of God.
This means, for present purposes, that the fundamental insights
expressed in the Bible came into being without benefit of the concept, or the type of thinking, represented by the more modern
term *nature,* and is therefore historically not basic to it. Only much
later did this remarkable idea become a component of religious
thought in the Judaeo-Christian tradition.*

Now as to the term "God," the situation is reversed. It is indigenous to religion, but does not belong to the vocabulary of
science. As used here the term is not intended to evoke an image
or face, or a mental construct of an entity or a being that *exists,*
in the sense that objects of scientific investigation exist. A different
way of thinking is called for here. We shall think of *God* as the
source of, and answer to, our ultimate questions and concerns, i.e.,
the answer to our whys, whences and whithers, and as the object of
our deepest faith and worship.

A well known saying of Luther's is pertinent here: "Whatever
then thy heart clings to and relies upon, that is properly thy god."
Now men's hearts cling to a large variety of things for support in
life. There are therefore many gods upon whom men pin their
hopes, such as humanity, one's own self, nature, one's country or
race; particular ways of life such as democracy or communism,

---

* Even today theologians disagree about the role the idea of nature
should play in Christian thought. This shows up in the variety of attitudes
toward "natural theology," in discussions of naturalism vs. supernaturalism,
in the emphasis upon history as the main locus of God's activity, and so on.

business, science, religion, education; values, sex, money, knowledge; theological images of God. For many people, however, reason and experience have shown that these are all inadequate as final determiners of their fate, and inadequate as either sources or objects of ultimate faith and love. Sooner or later they all fail. "God" then means the *God* beyond all such gods,* and beyond the conceptions or images of divinity that have evolved among the multitudinous formalized religions of mankind. I mean Being itself, the God of "radical monotheism." [4] Many men and women have encountered this God.

To summarize at this point, in an important sense science may be regarded as a relationship of men to nature, and religion as a relationship to God. In many ways these relationships are utterly unlike, while in others they are surprisingly similar. In the main, though not exclusively, religion—at least its Christian manifestation—is a deeply personal I-and-Thou relationship, whereas science is for the most part an impersonal I-and-It relationship.

How basically different these relationships are may be seen by a consideration of how scientific and religious questions respectively come to be answered; and how different in kind are the understandings the answers represent. In science one observes by the senses or with instruments, one measures and experiments; in religion one worships and prays, trusts, yields, serves and loves. In the former one experiments, i.e., "takes hold" of what is investigated and intervenes in its natural course of events, by imposing controls, suppressing some causal factors and abetting others. Thus one deliberately manipulates nature, so to speak, and wrings information out of it. In religion one cannot do anything like this. As many witnesses down through the ages have testified, there one *is grasped* and *given* insight—"by grace." One does not make control experiments. One responds, adores, obeys—and the understanding that comes is not achieved or contrived.

5 · FAITH

There is a word that inevitably makes its appearance in discussions of "science and religion" and is unfortunately thoroughly

* Consider also Tillich's provocative expression: the "God above God" or "the God above the God of theism." [3]

misunderstood, namely *faith.* The "believer" is alleged to be obliged
to "believe," and accept religious assertions, such as a creed, by
"blind faith," especially in situations where he finds it impossible
to support that belief by reason. Nothing could be farther from
the truth. It means no such thing—certainly not in the Judaeo-
Christian tradition. Rather *religious faith* is the name of the fundamental relationship between men and God. Its meaning is that of
a man trusting God, and an entrusting, yielding, accepting, committing of himself to God. It is fundamentally an attitude, an orientation, a condition, a state of being. In its essence it is experiential,
and not speculative. It is not an intellectual assenting to prescribed
propositions, a submissive acceptance of doctrine. It is not what
one resorts to finally in desperation after ordinary means have
been found wanting. Nor does it renounce or compete with reason.
Rather it is the point of departure for reason, the relationship
within which the reasoning of religion is done. Indeed, as we shall
see, the proper functioning of the mind in faith involves and demands the use of reason—without inhibition.

Scientists should not find it difficult to understand these aspects
of religion, for science has somewhat similar ones. Certainly there
is "scientific faith," and it is a trusting confidence in basic physical
reality, in the reliability and intelligibility of nature, a relationship,
an attitude, orientation or state of being, a yielding and abandoning
of one's self—in this case to the lure, or beckoning pull, of nature
and its mysteries. This is why Whitehead has said so often that
"science is an enterprise in which reason is based on a faith,"
rather than one which has faith based on reason. This is why he
can say that "it is essentially an antirationalist movement, based
upon an instinctive conviction and a naive faith," and that "this
faith cannot be justified by an inductive generalization." "It
springs," he says, "from direct inspection of the nature of things
so disclosed in our own immediate present experience" and "is
impervious to the demand for a consistent rationality." [5] This
scientific faith is not, any more than religious faith, a blind
credulity or a "blind taking things by faith," a submissive acceptance of propositions or a renouncing of reason. Rather it is a relationship between men and nature within which scientists do
their scientific reasoning.

Religion and science differ not in that the one has a faith and the other does not, but in that the objects of their faith are different and that in the latter—particularly in the Judaeo-Christian tradition—it has that added dimension of depth and ultimacy we spoke of earlier, that makes it radically different in quality.[6] To the so-called *believer* religious faith really matters, in the deep, all-involving sense that his very selfhood depends upon it; for it is in the faith relationship that God becomes existentially meaningful and man thereby becomes truly and fully himself. Without it he would be an utter stranger lost in the universe, without significance or purpose; and this would be tantamount to not *being* at all. In the light of such a faith all other faiths seem preliminary, partial, and of secondary importance—no matter how important they may be on other grounds.

Another way to put it is that while science *rests upon* a faith, Christianity *is* a faith—a radical faith. It is a fact not without significance that the technical vocabulary of science does not include the word *faith,* whereas in that of Christianity it is central. If it is ever mentioned in a treatise on the philosophy and methodology of science, it is only incidental, while in those devoted to Christianity it is ever-present, at the very core of the discussion. In the one it is *implicit,* in the other *explicit.* A man can be a good scientist, I suppose, without being conscious of having a scientific faith. Indeed many scientists deny that science requires faith *—so strange or undesirable does the use of the term seem to some of them. On the other hand no one can remain unaware of it in religion. For faith is the stuff out of which religion is fashioned.

6 · FAITH AND BELIEF

Unfortunately, in the English vocabulary of religion *faith* has taken on two distinct meanings, with much consequent confusion. More fortunately, in Latin two words are available, *fiducia* and *fides.*[7] The former refers to faith as trust and confidence, a "believing in" something or someone. By contrast the latter refers to a cognitive "believing that" something is true. Thus far I have used

* Although I suspect that such denial indicates a lack of understanding of the basic meaning of faith, scientific or otherwise.

the word *faith* only in the first, *fiducia,* sense and I shall continue to do so.* For the second, *fides,* I shall use the term *belief.*

With this semantic differentiation in mind I now make two observations. First, in religion—certainly in Christianity—*both* faith and belief take on truly momentous significance, in the sense that they *matter* with an existential urgency and reflect ultimate concern in an experience of depth. Second, in religion basic faith and basic belief are intermingled and interdependent to an extent quite unknown in science. To illustrate these matters let us consider a recently formulated affirmation of Christian faith-and-belief, the so-called *Statement of Faith* adopted by the new denomination, The United Church of Christ, that came into being in 1959 as the result of a merger of the Congregational-Christian Churches and the Evangelical and Reformed Church. It is presented on the next page. Note that it is first of all a confession of a trusting, committing faith, of a *believing in* God. "We believe in God." But it is also a confession of belief, a *believing that* God is good, and a witnessing to what God does in His goodness. It is evident here that the basic faith and the concomitant beliefs are inextricably entwined and interdependent, and that both matter deeply and are of ultimate significance existentially.

Now in science I can see nothing like this kind of a compound of fundamental faith and belief, welded together in necessary, indissoluble union and interdependence. Clearly the nature of science is very different from that of religion in this respect. Perhaps this is so because the basic faith of science is much less momentous existentially, much less consequential in life, involving far less of the scientist's personal being, and very much less specifically implicative of belief.

Some of the scientist's (and philosopher's) beliefs, e.g., that nature is a cosmos rather than chaos, are, of course, intimately related to his attitude of faith in nature as being dependable, and to some extent predictable rather than capricious. It is difficult to see how they would make sense otherwise. Certainly the faith implies the cosmos belief and vice versa. However, as one looks at

---

* This seems to be consistent with biblical usage which overwhelmingly identifies faith as being *fiducia,* a *believing in,* with all this implies with regard to commitment and loyalty.

STATEMENT OF FAITH
OF THE UNITED CHURCH OF CHRIST [8]

We believe in God, the Eternal Spirit, Father of our Lord Jesus Christ and our Father, and to His deeds we testify:

He calls the worlds into being, creates man in his own image and sets before him the ways of life and death.

He seeks in holy love to save all people from aimlessness and sin.

He judges men and nations by his righteous will declared through prophets and apostles.

In Jesus Christ, the man of Nazareth, our crucified and risen Lord, he has come to us and shared our common lot, conquering sin and death and reconciling the world to himself.

He bestows upon us his Holy Spirit, creating and renewing the Church of Jesus Christ, binding in covenant faithful people of all ages, tongues, and races.

He calls us into his Church to accept the cost and joy of discipleship, to be his servants in the service of men, to proclaim the gospel to all the world and resist the powers of evil, to share in Christ's baptism and eat at his table, to join him in his passion and victory.

He promises to all who trust him forgiveness of sins and fullness of grace, courage in the struggle for justice and peace, his presence in trial and rejoicing, and eternal life in his kingdom which has no end.

Blessing and honor, glory and power be unto him. Amen.

other scientific beliefs, e.g., those about conservation, or the Newtonian generalizations, this seems not to be the case. The basic scientific faith does not specifically imply these particular doctrines; nor would it seem to lose its meaning and significance if they were abandoned in favor of others. This would not create a particularly upsetting problem either intellectually or existentially. Not too much would be at stake. Clearly the situation in science with regard to the relationship of faith and beliefs is different from that prevailing in religion.

7 · CONCEPTUAL CONTENT OF SCIENCE AND RELIGION

Early in this chapter we pointed out that one way to characterize science and religion differentially is to note the kinds of fundamental questions they ask and the basic concerns expressed by them. Now we should look at these again, this time more especially with respect to the kinds of answers that have come out of science and religion respectively.

The answers of science are of course so well known that we need not exhibit them here in any detail. They are embodied in the substantive content of the separate sciences: on the one hand the vast bodies of experimentally determined factual knowledge found in the many handbooks and critical tables, and on the other the correlating overarching symbolic systems called theories. All this scientific knowledge is about various aspects of nature, and about the functional interrelations of its parts. By and large it is not about the scientist himself, and his desire to obtain it does not spring from personal concerns about himself. It represents the attempt to know, understand and use what is beyond and essentially independent of him.

How different the answers of religion are may be illustrated by the assertions of the *Statement of Faith*. To be sure, all of them are about God, a reality beyond and independent of man. But they are about God in relation to man, not about God in isolation, not about God as an object of "objective" investigation. What they assert is not how God looks, or what his metaphysical attributes are, but what he does. He "creates man in his own image and sets before him the ways of life and death," "seeks in holy love to save all people," "judges men and nations." In Jesus Christ he came among men to "conquer sin and death." He "calls," "promises," and "forgives." In short God is good and does good, and can be believed in. *We* can have faith in Him. *We* are very much in the picture of concerns.

Of course, while these beliefs pertain explicitly to God or God-in-relation-to-man, they have important implications for doctrines of man, and the world. Thus man is a being who is believed to be capable of responding to or rejecting divine love, of loving or hating, of building or destroying, and so on. More than that, man is recognized to be a creature upon whom God makes demands and who is responsible to God for his life and work. And the world is looked upon as a place where man has been placed by God to live to a purpose, and where God Himself acts in creative love with divine purpose.

If then the *Statement of Faith* is at all accurate as an expression of Christian faith and beliefs, and I think it is, and if it is at all typical in its affirmations of distinctively religous insight and teachings, then what religion is concerned about and has to offer is categorically different from what is available through science.

Sometimes this categorical difference is lost sight of or obscured by the identity of the form of certain scientific and religious questions. Especially is this the case for those involving such terms as *why* and *should* and *must*. In both science and religion it may be asked: Why does this happen? Why should this be so? Why must things be done this way? * Clearly, however, very different kinds of answers are called for. In the case of science the *why* refers to natural causes discernible in or postulated for nature. Why does a bullet come out of a gun when the trigger is pulled? Because expanding gas pushes it out. Why does the bullet eventually fall to the earth? Because of gravity. Similarly questions involving such words as *should* and *must* refer to causal relationships. Why must a rocket be given a certain initial velocity if it is to "escape from the earth"? Why must water be *pumped* uphill, if it is to go uphill? Why should one be vaccinated for smallpox? What the answers are expected to tell is how we *should* or *must*

---

* Though there are many interpreters of science who say that science only attempts to discover *how* things happen, not *why*.

relate contemplated action to the relevant causal complex in order that the desired effect may be achieved.

In religion, however, questions of *why?* and why *should?* refer not to natural causes but to the mystery that still remains after science has given its answers, i.e., to the *whys* and *shoulds* of ultimate origin and destiny, meaning and value. Why and whence the causes? As we shall see more clearly later, the answers of religion refer to God. Why are the basic causal relationships the way they are? Because God so wills it. Why *should* men love one another? Because God so wills and demands. In this context the question Why should one be vaccinated for smallpox? involves a different *why,* and calls for a different kind of answer. Health is a value made sacred by God. Vaccination is for the purpose of maintaining one's own health, and of protecting that of others. The *should* refers not to a relating of oneself to natural law but to moral and ethical values, to ultimate concerns, and divine demands.

It is evident then that science and religion ask radically different questions and provide radically different answers even when the language employed does not itself suggest these categorical differences.

8 · DIFFERENT BUT NOT INCOMPATIBLE

Much more needs to be said about what science and religion are—and what they are not—but it may not be inappropriate to interrupt this analysis to ask whether any reason has appeared for supposing that the radical differences between science and religion noted thus far must necessarily make for incompatibility or antipathy. I feel, of course, that the answer is no. None has appeared. Controversy or incompatibility are not necessary concomitants of these differences. For one thing, there can be no genuine logical contradictions such as are possible among like categories, because science and religion represent two different types of concern, and different aspects or dimensions of life and thought. In the second place, they do not signify inherent antipathy of purpose or ideal. Surely there can be neither logical contradiction nor clash of ideals in accepting both a biological conception of life based on microscopic observations and chemical analyses, and a religious conception of it derived from living, and from reflection upon its meaning ultimately. Surely to study love, as an object of socio- logical or psychological investigation, cannot be inconsistent with or inimical to studying it as a gift of God. To think of man, for scientific purposes, in terms of levers, neural electric circuits, cybernetic feedbacks and controls, or chemical reactions, surely cannot of itself be incompatible with thinking of him for religious purposes as a "creature" or "child of God." To have preliminary concerns certainly cannot be inappropriate simply because one has ultimate concerns also. How can confession of faith in God and a belief in his fatherhood, such as are expressed in, say, the *State- ment of Faith,* be regarded as clashing with the faith and teachings of science?

Unfortunately, however, things do not always work out logically, and clashes do take place. Certainly this can happen when one or the other (or both) is misunderstood and misapplied, or has actually become distorted by aberrations. This has often happened in the past, and we shall have to look into this frankly and critically. We will be in a better position to do this, however, after we have studied other aspects of the nature of science and religion. In the meantime I would plead for a suspension of final judgment until much more of the evidence is in.

CHAPTER III

What Science and Religion Are Not

Stereotypes and Actualities

1 · A NEGATIVE APPROACH

In the preceding chapter the approach was positive in the attempt to characterize science and religion by pointing out some of their most distinctive fundamental features. Now the approach will be negative in the sense that certain commonly held notions will be examined that seem to me to be erroneous stereotypes that do not correspond to the actualities of science and religion. The discussion will focus in the main upon two such stereotypes, namely "the scientific method" and "divine revelation."

There can be no doubt that one of the distinguishing marks of science is its methodology. Indeed many interpreters of science regard this as its most characteristic feature. Unfortunately, however, what this has come to mean commonly gives an utterly false impression of what the processes of science really are. Similarly "divine revelation" certainly is one of the most significant distinguishing marks of religion—at least of Judaism and Christianity. If we would really understand them we must understand what is meant by the actualities of revelation—but not its stereotype.

2 · DOES "THE SCIENTIFIC METHOD" EXIST?

According to prevailing notions science is an intellectual machine, which, when one turns a crank called "the scientific method," inerrantly grinds out final truth with complete accuracy and certainty. This method is alleged to have certain "steps" that must be followed for success. Its thinking is regarded as exclusively logical

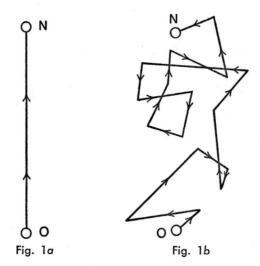

Fig. 1a   Fig. 1b

Two conceptions of scientific progress from an old to a new state of
knowledge: (a) alleged, (b) actual.

and its language as utterly precise and unambiguous. Nothing
could be farther from the truth. Far from being machine-like,
science is a characteristically human enterprise [1] that is intensely
personal, as well as social and communal. With all the strengths
and weaknesses this implies.

Consider for instance how the findings of science actually come
about. In Fig. 1, point O represents an "old" state of knowledge,
and N a new one. Progress from O to N is usually conceived as
being *forced* along an undeviating path, as illustrated by *a* of Fig. 1,
by the inexorable compulsions of "the scientific method." Actually,
of course, it comes about haltingly, circuitously, with many false
starts, and often illogically, as represented by Fig. 1b.

As a matter of fact, the straight line of *a* represents afterthoughts on how N *could* have been reached if the original development *had been* strictly logical. But this does not become apparent until afterwards. It is necessary, therefore, to recognize two
stages in the gaining of scientific knowledge, namely the pioneering
stage and the colonizing stage, in which prevailing methodologies
and procedures are in important respects very different. Frontier

science is exploratory and adventurous. Its ideas are tentative and always in flux. More often than not they are audacious guesses or vague hunches that rarely conform to orthodox patterns of thought and often seem illogical and thoroughly "unscientific." Here methods are tailored to particular problems and are determined largely by the demands and urgencies of the moment. Fig. 1b is symbolic of this frontier stage.

As in the case of a national frontier, sooner or later the pioneers are followed by the colonizers who consolidate gains, establish order, permanence and respectability, and replace the crooked paths by straight highways, Fig. 1a. In this stage ideas and methods conform more nearly to canons of orthodoxy and the hunch is replaced by the logical derivation and elegant "proof."

It is, of course, not difficult to understand why the popular mind is for the most part unaware of these different stages of scientific development, and why the one, that of the frontier, has virtually been lost sight of altogether. For one thing, most people get their knowledge of science from textbooks and more popular expositions that present science systematically, that exhibit the end product of its search rather than its beginnings, and that endeavor to show how things make sense and fit together reasonably. Quite commonly they show how particular items of knowledge (N) can be "derived" from earlier or more fundamental ones (O). In examinations in school or college we frequently ask students to "prove" something; for instance in physics, that the equation that describes uniformly accelerated motion * follows logically from basic postulates of classical mechanics, namely Newton's Laws of Motion. They may be asked *why* a moving body *should* have kinetic energy equal to an amount given by a certain mathematical formula.† Again what is expected is to show that this formula can be deduced from Newton's Laws. Unfortunately, authors and teachers usually fail to point out that these neat, direct, rather obvious derivations are for the most part afterthoughts that represent the way the colonizer thinks, whose task it is to systematize things intellectually, who must invoke logical deduction to regularize and authenticate what

---

* In simple form: $s = \frac{1}{2}at^2$, where s is the distance, a acceleration, and t time.

† Kinetic energy: $E_k = \frac{1}{2}mv^2$, where m is mass, and v is velocity.

may have emerged in the first place mostly by hunch or lucky guess.

In the student laboratory the same sort of thing is perpetrated. So-called experiments are set up that usually are not experiments at all, but rather only laboratory exercises designed to provide fully expected empirical verification—in foolproof manner and by the shortest possible logical route—of principles and laws that are already well known. Sad to say, the doing of these exercises rarely gives any hint of the painful intellectual travail and the long and often disappointing wanderings about in the wilderness of repeated failures that may have preceded the final successful break-through into the promised land of new knowledge.

Obviously there are good reasons for writing textbooks and designing laboratory work in this way. The fact is, however, that the result of it is to leave beginning students with utterly false impressions of the nature of science and its methodology.

There are two things that need to be said explicitly about *the* alleged scientific method, first, that there is no such thing, as it is commonly conceived, and, second, that whatever science may have by way of method is characterized not so much by the niceties and compulsions of formal deductive logic, as by the potencies and freedom of human imagination.

As for the first, it is a fact that science has many characteristic *methods,* not *one,* and that they are so varied that reference to them en masse by the usual stereotype is thoroughly misleading. What many physical scientists think about this is expressed pointedly by the late Professor P. W. Bridgman of Harvard University, one of the world's most distinguished physicists, in the following oft-quoted, provocative statement:

> The scientific method, as far as it is a method, is nothing more than doing one's damnedest with one's mind, no holds barred. What primarily distinguishes science from other intellectual enterprises in which the right answer has to be obtained is not method but the subject matter.[2]

What this means is that science has no unique recipe for concocting a scientific brew, and one that assures satisfactory results and guarantees against failure. Many inexperienced graduate students have been genuinely puzzled and disturbed by what seemed to them to be the unmethodical and "unscientific" procedures of active, experienced investigators in a research laboratory. They were unable to discern in what was going on around them any "system" even remotely suggestive of "the scientific method," with its alleged necessarily sequential "steps," about which they had heard so much in high school or college. To discover that competent and well known scientists go about their business quite oblivious of the existence of this method they had been led to regard as the most important characteristic of science, was a most revealing—even though painfully disillusioning—experience.

As a distinguished psychologist once remarked, "It is astonishing how few people realize that the methods of science are in the main *ad hoc* in nature." He was, of course, quite right. The particular method a scientist uses at any time is determined largely by the problem he is tackling, and by *his* own past experience, temperament and imagination. Another commentator, Professor F. S. C. Northrop of Yale, has this to say:

> The emphasis upon the primacy of the character of the problem results in the relativity of scientific method to the type of problem before one and the stage of inquiry with respect to that type of problem. It follows that there is no one scientific method and that to talk about scientific method apart from the specification of the specific stage of inquiry for a given type of problem is as meaningless as to talk about either space by itself or time by itself, apart from the specification of the frame of reference from which each is determined.[3]

Of course, not all scientists seem to agree with Bridgman and Northrop. Many of them insist that science does have a *characteristic method,* that it has certain indispensable components— if not steps—such as the gathering of data, the formulation of concepts and general relationships, the creation and use of hypotheses, and the deductive application of generalizations and hypotheses to particular situations. It seems to me, however, that this is a disagreement about terminology rather than about the nature of science and its methodology. That scientific methodology does include these very general processes as indispensable components is undeniable. But the point is that this is true of every other field of scholarship that seeks knowledge—including theology. It follows then that if it is defined in such general terms it certainly is not uniquely characteristic of natural science. To quote Bridgman again:

> The so-called scientific method is merely a special case of the method of intelligence, and any apparently unique characteristics are to be explained by the nature of the subject matter rather than ascribed to the nature of the method itself.[4]

The first observation to be made about "the scientific method" is then that there is no such thing—*as it is ordinarily conceived.*

It may be that this discussion of "the scientific method" and especially of the difference between the pioneering and colonization stages of scientific development will seem rather abstract to readers who are not themselves scientists. Perhaps no one ever really comes to understand these matters fully until he has himself participated in the scientific enterprise, until he has himself experienced success and failure, elation and dejection, in the search for new scientific knowledge. But one may develop a "feel" for it by talking with investigators about their work or reading their diaries and biographies. Sometimes, though only rarely, their technical publications give an account of the circuitous path their search followed before the final goal could be reached. The general reader is referred especially to a series of source books prepared under the editorship of James B. Conant for the specific purpose of providing more adequate accounts of the realities of scientific investigation than were easily accessible before. Dr. Conant's little book *On Understanding Science* will also be found to be helpful for obtaining a more concrete interpretation of my more abstract discussion. The book *The Art of Scientific Investigation,* by Beveridge of Cambridge University, is also recommended. Finally I suggest that occasionally a novelist has caught the vision of scientific endeavor and been able to portray it rather well. C. P. Snow's *The Search* and Morton Thompson's *The Cry and the Covenant* are cases in point. The latter is based on the life and work of Ignaz Semmelweis and his heroic but unsuccessful attempt to eradicate the dread disease of puerperal fever. Of special interest for present purposes is the account of his long, arduous, discouraging, circuitous search

for the cause of the disease. In the end the answer looked simple
—to him—but not so before the end.[5]

3 · LOGIC AND LINGUISTIC DEFINITION IN SCIENCE

The second observation to be made about the methods of science
is that contrary to prevailing opinion science does not constitute a
paradigm or model of formal logical thinking, in the sense that at
every step of the way its thought is controlled by the canons of inductive and deductive logic. Clearly, if it were there could be no intellectual wanderings such as are depicted by Fig. 1*b*—unless, of
course, science were purely empirical, which manifestly it is not.

Before developing this it should be emphasized that science is
a thoroughly rational enterprise. It demands rigorous thought
and renounces sloppy or wishful thinking. There is no room in
science for him who would by-pass reason. The point to be made
here, however, is that reason and rational procedure are not what
they are often imagined to be. They far transcend the limits of
formal logic. If we are to understand the true nature of science in
this regard, we must realize two things. First, most scientists are
far from being expert in the niceties of formal logic. They do not
need it very much in their business. Indeed I would assert that
most of them are the kind of people who become quite impatient
with logical minutiae. Moreover, only rarely do they study logic
explicitly. Typically they know no more about it than they learned
in high school geometry. Rarely, if ever, does scientific thought
proceed by logical syllogisms. Such logic as is required is for the
most part of a very simple kind, and even that is largely hidden
in the more or less automatic processes of mathematical manipulation. About all that is demanded in practice is that a scientist use
"good reasoning" and common sense and that he not be guilty
of obvious logical contradiction. Physics is commonly regarded
as the most highly developed of the sciences from the viewpoint
of logic. And yet it is well known that mathematicians, many of
whom *are* logicians professionally, are prone to shake their heads
in wonderment and despair at the atrocious logic of physicists in
general. But this does not in the least worry the physicists, who
merrily go on with their business regardless. And I dare say the

situation is no different for chemists, biologists, psychologists or any other scientists. Scientists are for the most part ordinary human beings—albeit usually fairly intelligent ones—who are doing their best with their minds, no holds barred, even without benefit of the austerities of impeccable logic.

What is actually much more important than skill in formal logic—and indeed indispensable—in scientific thinking is creative, *imaginative* reasoning. Now to reason imaginatively does not mean to eschew logic; but it may at times mean disregarding *conventional* logic. It has happened more than once in the history of science that scientists have been able to make progress only by ignoring the logical situation, and deliberately bypassing a logical contradiction or impasse and going ahead in spite of it. It has been said that one of the most amazing spectacles in the history of ideas is that of the fraternity of physicists early in the second quarter of the twentieth century, blithely thinking of light part of the time as waves and part of the time as particles—even though so to think then seemed utterly illogical, by conventional canons of logic. An analogous situation appeared somewhat later, when atoms and molecules that had for a long time been regarded as particles were discovered to have wave characteristics. In terms of the conventional logic of categories, how can a particle be like a wave? How this problem was resolved we cannot discuss now. The point is, however, that at the time this logical contradiction was not allowed to stop progress and was for the time being bypassed. Clearly, then, scientific thinking is not controlled by strict logic, but rather is imaginatively independent of it—employing it or not according to circumstances.

Imaginative thinking means also thinking where formal logic is more or less helpless and has but little if anything to offer; where ideas do not follow inexorably from others that have already been established; where no recipe or "method" exists for guiding thought from one phase to the next. There are many such situations in science. Let us consider one that is typical, namely the formation of hypotheses. Sooner or later, either before or after the scientist has made observations and then wishes to explain them, he endeavors to construct an hypothesis. This is for him one of the critical stages in the investigation he is conducting. What is called for then does not usually follow coercively from his observations or experiments. He needs an idea or thought pattern that transcends the concepts directly resident in, or derivable from, his data. For if the desired hypothesis is to be acceptable, it must explain more than he knows at that moment. It must comprehend and suggest to him other possibilities of knowledge, other observations that might lead to that knowledge and be verifiable as such.

Now "the scientific method" is often said to have four components, namely observation, inductive generalization, deductive prediction, and experimental verification. The second of these four steps is alleged to be governed by the logical process of induction. Indeed induction is frequently asserted to be *the* most characteristic feature of science, aside from experimentation. According to this view of science it is induction that comes to the rescue of the scientist at the critical moment when he needs an hypothetical idea. It is alleged to be a logical process by which the weight of a large accumulation of data and the evidence from the study of many similar cases forces upon him a general idea or generalization that covers all the particular ones that his investigation has uncovered. This then is the way an hypothesis is supposed to be born *logically*. Unfortunately—or probably fortunately—this is not the way it works in practice. Probably no hypothesis was ever brought forth in this neat manner. Moreover, in all probability the process of induction as it is commonly conceived does not even exist as a component of scientific methodology. Most scientists would, I suspect, deny that they know anything about it, or that they ever used it or heard of anyone else who used it in scientific work.

How then are hypotheses born? It is a complex process that may in any given case involve a large variety of mental processes: guesses and hunches, "cutting and trying," thinking by analogies, creation of pictures and models, statistical analysis and curve-fitting, closely reasoned criticism, tentative intuitive acceptance or rejection, deductive exploration of possible consequences, comparison with existing explanations, and still others. At every stage the scientist employs reason. But, and this is the point to be emphasized here, there is a creative, imaginative component of the process that is neither determined nor limited by formal logic.

What is demanded of the hypothesis first of all is that it explain what is known, that it conform to the data in hand. But what this amounts to is the "seeing of a pattern" and this is in essence a synthesizing act of the imagination. But before such an hypothetical, explanatory pattern can be accepted it must be examined critically to determine whether it does in fact conform to the data. If not it must be modified, or a new one sought. As N. R. Hanson [6] has shown, a process variously called *reduction, abduction* or *retroduction* is involved in many such situations, requiring the construction of an hypothesis, which unfortunately cannot be described here in detail. And though this is a thoroughly rational technique, it certainly involves mental processes that can be described properly only as being creatively imaginative.

The following quotation from Philipp Frank further emphasizes this point:

> The main activity of science . . . consists in the invention of symbols from which our experience can be logically derived. This system is the work of the creative imagination which acts on the basis of our experience. The work of the scientist is probably not fundamentally different from the work of the poet.[7]

While this statement taken out of context needs qualifying interpretation, it does call attention to an aspect of scientific thought that is lost sight of much too often.

This is why Polanyi has suggested that if there actually are any typical "steps" in scientific method they might well be designated as preparation, incubation, illumination and verification.[8] A most unfortunate consequence of the prevalence of the stereotyped notions of scientific method is that it has tended to obscure one of science's most potent sources of strength, namely that of human imagination and intuition, wherein it is remarkably akin to the humanities and religion. There can be little doubt that most of the truly great and revolutionary ideas of science came into being intuitively during periods of revelatory insight, rather than by syllogistic or inductive logic.

Of course, intuition or imagination unguided by formal logic plays important roles elsewhere also in the scientific enterprise. While we speak blithely of the deductive process of working out the implications of an hypothesis, in practice this is far from a formally logical procedure. It always involves an imaginative appraisal of the possibilities and probabilities for implication, and of the direction the actual deduction should take. Then when the deductions from the hypothesis have been derived, it requires a great deal of imagination ordinarily to work out methods of experimental verification. Often this means formulating new concepts, and having to devise completely new apparatus and measuring techniques. Furthermore, a good hypothesis often implies much more than may at first be anticipated. Sometimes it opens up completely new fields, and in the recognition of these it is the imagination, much more than deductive reason, that is the discoverer.

Related to the logic-machine concept is the popular notion that the language of science is utterly precise and unambiguous, and that it specializes in punctilious, incisive definitions. This too is but a caricature of the facts. Language that is precise to that extent is no doubt useful and indeed necessary in a discipline like mathematics, that engages in logical deduction as one of its primary tasks. But for an enterprise like science, in which free, imaginative and non-logical thinking is typically the order of the day, what is needed is more elasticity than rigidity of concepts, more inclusive adumbration than exclusive delimitation of ideas, less sharp definition and more lucid circumlocution.

The fact is that scientists define their concepts precisely in words much less frequently than is commonly supposed. For the most part they extract the meanings of concepts from their context and then "define" them by mathematical symbols, i.e., formulas or equations, which transmit meaning largely by showing relations with other concepts. Similarly they communicate meanings contextually more than by formal definition. When scientists want to know the meaning of a new term introduced by a colleague they talk with him about his work which led up to the need for the new idea. As he tells them of particular observations and experiments he has made, his meaning begins to emerge. Professor James K. Senior,[9] of the department of Chemistry of the University of Chicago, in an extremely illuminating article on the language of science, expresses the opinion that ostensive definition is much more common among scientists than is intensive definition. By "ostensive definition" he seems to mean informal definition through conversation and writing. This is what I have spoken of as contextual clarification. By way of illustration he asserts that he has used the term "hydrolysis" for twenty years without ever seeing a definition of it. His teacher depended upon him to use his "imagination or insight or intuition" to grasp its meaning as the phenomenon of hydrolysis was studied and discussed. And now he in turn expects the same of his students. This he believes is altogether typical in science. He states interestingly

> I have found that if in talking to chemists I were to restrict myself to terms which they (or for that matter I) could define by intension, I would be tongue-tied. When I rely not on their ability to give verbal definitions, but on the thoroughness of their conditioning and on the close resemblance between that conditioning and my own, I have no trouble at all.[10]

About the only people who deal extensively in presumably accurate intensive definitions are the writers of textbooks and the teachers of elementary courses, who function to some extent as the colonizers and systematizers of whom we have spoken earlier. What should be remembered is that this is not representative of the researching scientists or pioneers.

What is required of scientific writing is maximum clarity of exposition, but this cannot be achieved by the purveying of precisely worded definitions. There are at least two reasons for this. In the first place, to be most meaningful in science a term must evoke images of operations or happenings in laboratory or field. Since these are always rather complex, this necessarily means approximate verbal definition. It signifies also that the meaning of a term changes as it is applied to different experimental situations. Consider, for instance, the shift in operational meaning of the term *length,* as we apply it successively to the following specific concepts: distance from the earth to a spiral nebula, diameter of the sun, distance from Chicago to New York, the dimensions of a house, the diameter of a hair, the size of chromosomes, the wave length of yellow light, the diameter of the nucleus of the hydrogen atom. Here we have a whole gamut of lengths that differ tremendously in magnitude, the largest being billions of billions of billions of times larger than the smallest. The operations by which one measures these distances are just as vastly different. And the mental operations by which one manipulates them in one's thinking are no less unlike. Clearly then the term *length* is far from being precise or even uni-valued. It has a whole spectrum of meaning and I suspect it is a continuous spectrum. Obviously then a conventional kind of definition of length is quite inadequate for conveying its meaning.

In the second place, the meanings of terms shift from time to time with the increase of scientific knowledge. To return to the term *length,* the significance and conceptual content of it changed vastly when Einstein helped us to see that the *physical* length of a moving body changes with the speed of the body relative to a frame of reference. Never again can we think of length only in the old static terms. The same is true of the concepts of time and space. Similarly the idea of energy changed radically when it became known that it could be transmuted into mass, and vice versa. Now a term would be useless if its meaning did not shift with the times, i.e., if we had to devise a new term every time a concept changed significantly. Thought would be fettered by precise and fixed definitions. Progress in science would be very, very difficult without a judicious amount of vagueness and mobility of scientific concepts.

If all this be true, it is evident that the popular conception of science as an intellectual machine that has built into it automatic logical devices for the avoidance of error and for the identification of infallible truth, is erroneous. The stages by which scientific insight are attained are not predetermined by logical necessity. Its modes of thought and linguistic expression are more creatively imaginative than formally logical, and successful communication depends more upon a common background and conditioning, and therefore on co-understanding,[11] than upon formal precision of language.

4 · DIVINE REVELATION

Now let us turn to the stereotype that bedevils our understanding of religion, namely the widely prevailing conception of revelation. It too is alleged to be a sure-fire way by which final and inerrant truth comes to man, by a short cut after the manner of Fig. 1*a*. But, alas, this is a false picture, as the facts of life amply attest. Consider for example any of the great insights of the Judaeo-Christian tradition, such as that God is One, is Creator, is Father, and is Love. Surely the history of their development must be portrayed, if it is to be done accurately, by the tortuous, laboring, meandering and circuitous path of Fig. 1*b*. They simply did not appear full blown. The revelatory process and experience extended over a long period of time, and the route certainly was not straight.

As popularly conceived, revelation is a process by which God hands down specific information about Himself, in the form of inerrant propositions or doctrines. God is thought of as dictating, so to speak, to a passive secretary or a human typewriter. But this is not the way much of contemporary theology thinks of it, neither Catholic nor Protestant.[12] Rather it is God-given understanding, an opening of the mind and heart, not the imparting of specific information. It is a sharpening of vision and the seeing of perspective, not a direct increment of doctrine. It is an encounter between God and man in life and work, in the history of peoples as well as in the personal experience of individuals. It is knowledge *of* God, that may lead to, but is not itself theological knowledge *about* God. It is God making *Himself* known and man coming to know *Him*. Revelation may be experienced as a sudden bursting forth of insight in a particular life situation or encounter-event, or it may be the gradual growth of understanding that comes to individual or community after such events and as the result of long experience and learning.

Revelation is what happened to Abraham when he became aware of God's call to leave his home—and responded. It is what happened to Moses when he encountered God through the burning bush and became aware of a solemn duty under God toward his people—and responded. It happened to Isaiah when in the temple he "saw the Lord sitting upon a throne, high and lifted up," and heard the voice of God saying "Whom shall I send?"—and he replied, "Here I am! Send me." It was a revelatory experience for Job when he heard God speak through a whirlwind and was able thereafter to say, "I have uttered what I did not understand. . . . I had heard of thee by the hearing of the ear, but now my eye

sees thee." Revelation is what was experienced by Saul of Tarsus
on the way to Damascus, when he became the new man Paul; by
St. Francis of Assisi, by Martin Luther and many another mighty
man of God. It is what happens also, I should say, to many ordinary, humble men and women when there come to them strong
convictions as to the way they should go under God, or when they
come to see more clearly what formerly was very dim, namely,
His love, goodness, holiness and will.

Apparently, however, the term "divine revelation" refers, in
its most basic meaning current in theology today, to communal
rather than solitary experience, to great revelatory events in the
history of peoples, more than to revelatory moments in the lives
of individuals. Professor Daniel Day Williams has put it cogently
thus: "To speak of revelation in the prophets and in Christ . . .
is to speak of those happenings in human history which have so
opened our eyes and so transformed our minds that the disclosure of God to man has taken place." [13] From this point of view
the Exodus was a truly revelatory event for Israel—and for much
of mankind. So was the experience at Mount Sinai. For the Christian community the most revealing experience was the cluster of
events centered in the person of Jesus Christ. As a result of it nature, man, and God took on new meaning. The world and life have
never been the same since then—for the men and women who
knew Jesus personally, and no less so for those who followed
them and know him through the "Holy Spirit."

How then did Christianity come by such insights and beliefs as
are affirmed in the *Statement of Faith?* If we say "by revelation"
we do not refer to some sort of extra-sensory supra-auditory perception by which God is heard to be speaking forth specific religious information or doctrines, but rather to revelatory experience. And this experience has been—and continues to be—so real
and tremendous that because of it Christians speak of themselves
as having been "born again." This revelatory experience was above
all an individual and communal encounter, a coming to know God,
an entering into the faith relationship with God. Out of this then
came the understanding and beliefs that constitute "knowledge of
God" as a living, acting God, and these beliefs came for the most
part slowly and through long and arduous travail. There is here

no renunciation of the ordinary processes of perception and reason, no "acceptance by blind faith," as is so often supposed.

5 · AUTHORITY

Another aspect of the stereotyped conception has to do with *authority* and *authoritarianism*. Since the truth of beliefs is guaranteed by divine revelatory fiat they become authoritative in the arbitrary sense, and this means that they *must* be accepted in humble submission to that authority. Admittedly this does represent rather accurately what has been the attitude that characterizes much of religion, including large sectors of Christendom. Nevertheless I would say that history clearly shows that the authority of the basic Christian doctrines and beliefs—such as are expressed in a creedal formulation like the *Statement of Faith*—does not stem fundamentally from ecclesiastical edicts, as is commonly supposed, but from their compelling nature as truthful descriptions or testimonies of what many men and women have known has happened to them, and of the trusting confidence and hopes that have developed among them. Revelation is authoritative because it actually reveals, not because it has been decreed to be so.

6 · LOGIC AND LINGUISTIC DEFINITION IN RELIGION

The situation in religion with regard to logic is not unlike that in science. In the minds of those who believe in the stereotype of revelation, logic plays a tremendously important role, for it is held that once the initial revelation has been vouchsafed to man, thereafter its various doctrinal implications follow inerrantly if the canons of deductive logic are not violated. Again we encounter a logic-machine sort of concept. Deviational thinking is attributed in this view to illogical reasoning caused by ineptness, or stupidity, or insincerity, or sin. But I say this is no more true a picture than the corresponding one of science. Actually religion, like science, has both a pioneering and a colonizing stage in its search for insight. In neither field are successive steps of development compelled or foreordained by pure logic, though in both sound logical reasoning is indispensable. In both imaginative reasoning is still more important. In both advance in understanding requires "doing one's utmost with one's mind, no holds barred." In neither is there any way to avoid or circumnavigate this.

And the same remarks apply to the language of religion. At its best it is imaginatively free and expressively flexible, rather than fixedly precise. In religion too definitions are for the most part ostensive rather than intensive. Here too meanings come out of contextual clarification, and one has to depend upon co-understanding and similarity of background and conditioning.

CHAPTER IV

Science and Religion as Social and Communal Enterprises

They Are Intensely Human

1 · THE EMERGING PORTRAIT OF SCIENCE

In saying what science is, we have taken cognizance of its being a body of knowledge—but have insisted that it is more than that. We have noted that it is often spoken of as a way of knowing—but have seen that this means much more than is implied by the stereotype of "the scientific method." We have observed that to appreciate adequately the methodology of science we must be aware of two different aspects or stages of scientific development, designated respectively the frontier stage and the stage of colonization. Finally, we saw that the role of logic in scientific thought is commonly misrepresented, and that what is at least as important —if not more so—is the creative imagination. The picture of science that emerges is then one of an intensely human enterprise, as opposed to the impersonal automatic machine conception of it. There are other aspects of this human quality of science that need pointing out.

2 · SCIENCE, A SOCIAL ENTERPRISE

Science is not only a human, but more particularly a social enterprise—that is, one of sharing, cooperation, and of interaction of people. Among students the following question always generates considerable interest and discussion: Is a one-man physics possible? Could a completely isolated man with great intelligence and unlimited material resources, as well as unlimited time, develop a body of knowledge such as we now call physics? Almost invariably students reply with a *yes*. The lone scientist could, they argue, make observations, devise apparatus and processes of experimentation, measurement and theorizing. In time he could obtain all the data and curves required to establish all the laws and principles of physics, and construct the appropriate theories to explain them. Experienced physicists, however, reply with a *no*. They point out that our lone physicist could not be sure of his results if he could not check his data and conclusions against those of other physicists. He might remain blissfully unaware of systematic errors due to his own idiosyncrasies. Instruments and solitary intelligence do not of themselves guarantee accuracy.

It is in this mutuality and interdependence that the so-called "objectivity" of science has its deepest roots. This objectivity results from science's insistence upon empirical evidence and confirmation. A point to be emphasized, however, is that objectivity cannot be achieved by a solitary individual, but only socially, i.e., when the observations and experiments of one scientist have been validated reciprocally through repetition by others. This is why science never considers new findings to be established until they have been confirmed by more than one observer. It has developed no way of obviating this need for mutual validation and confirmation among scientists. A term that is highly suggestive here, and that may be regarded as a synonym of "objectivity," is "intersubjective testability." [1] It calls attention to the fundamental necessity of interpersonal exchanges and checks in the testing and confirmation processes of science.

Consideration of so hypothetical and artificial a situation as that of a completely isolated scientist brings into the open many facts about the actual, existential science that rarely are noticed or mentioned, and yet are of great importance for an adequate understanding of science. Thus there are actually no supermen who could go it alone, who could do everything themselves. To conduct the work of science requires an amazing number of different kinds of people with varying talents, skills, and interests. We became acutely conscious of this during the last war, when it became necessary to establish in isolated locations throughout our country completely new science towns, e.g., Los Alamos of which we have all heard so much. They were, and still are, *science* communities in the sense that their sole reason for existence was to carry on scientific work.

The life and operation of such a community requires an amazing number of different kinds of people and talents. These include at least the experimentalist and theorist, the lone researcher and team researcher, the critic and referee, the philosopher and historian of science, the teaching scientist, the research director, the research manager and business officer, the personnel officer, the report writer, the editor, the translator, the statistician, the liaison officer, and the instrument designer, all of whom must be scientists. In such situations men discover how inextricably the various sciences are bound together, how the physicist needs the help of the chemist and vice versa. How both need the engineer, the psychologist, the biologist, the medical man, as well as the economist. And all of them become keenly aware of their dependence upon nonscientists such as the plumber, the electrician, the secretary, and last but not least the "science widow" who keeps the soup warm when her husband is late.

Here, too, one becomes conscious of the multiplicity of underlying psychological drives that lead men to become scientists and that affect their decisions thereafter, as well as of the intense feelings of *personal* dependence upon their fellows. It becomes apparent that not only are there no supermen who *can* go it alone, but that probably there are none who would *want* to go it alone if they could. Not only does the scientist always have his limitations, necessitating mutual aid, but he knows it. Not only does he need help in making experiments and interpreting their results, but he is conscious of that need. The recognition of it constitutes part of his professional equipment. Moreover, sooner or later he wants to exchange and share new ideas and findings with fellow scientists. He knows that if there is to be progress he must build on the results of others and must, in turn, make contributions upon which others can build. He realizes that he needs the criticism of his fellows, but also he craves their approval. Few scientists would do research, I believe, if they could not publish their results and get due credit for them, or could not see socially beneficial consequences flowing from their work, or were not motivated socially in other ways that certainly are operative in our present science enterprise. Science is undeniably social.

3 · THE GREAT AND THE ORDINARY MEN OF SCIENCE

There is another typically human aspect of science that usually remains unnoticed. The conventional images of both past and present science result from using lenses that bring into focus mostly its great towering figures, leaving much of the picture unseen. This is unfortunate, just as it would be if one saw America only in terms of its great heroes—George Washington and Abraham Lincoln, Ralph Waldo Emerson and William James—thus seeing it only partially. Full understanding would require that the common man and his way of life be known also. The same is true of science. To see it only as the creation of its geniuses—Galileo, Newton, Harvey, Pasteur, Einstein—is not enough, for there is in fact also the science of its lesser devotees, the ordinary, garden variety of scientists who are almost unknown except in their own localities or to fellow workers in their own particular narrow subfields of science, who are not at the very forefront of modern research, and who in a whole lifetime publish only a few papers of restricted significance, whose work and way of life are rather different from those of the geniuses, but who nevertheless are real scientists.[2]

Now to depict the common-man aspect of science clearly, and to demonstrate what many of us feel—namely, that it is significantly different from the better-known science of the masters—would require much more factual knowledge than is now available. It is probable, however, that if this were studied carefully, many of the conventional descriptions and "models" of science would have to be revised extensively. It would become clear how completely unsatisfactory it is to say that "the scientist does it this way, but not that," or "the scientist believes this, not that." It would be evident that there is no such thing as *the scientist,* that this term must necessarily stand for many kinds of scientists, whose ways of thinking and habitual modes of experimentation and research differ widely, and among whom there are many degrees of sophistication with regard to the purposes, goals, and methodology of science, and many fundamental disagreements about both the content and meaning of its principles, concepts, and generalizations. And especially, I suspect, such study would reveal pronounced dissimilarity between the patterns of intellectual strategy and tactics prevailing in the common-man science and those of the great-man science.

Historical analysis [3] would probably reveal also that the meandering onward flow of science is determined to a large extent by the rank and file, who, because of their persistent interests, carry exploration in particular fields to their logical conclusions long after the geniuses have lost interest and turned to other more enticing problems. It may show also that in the long run progress is facilitated by the damping and filtering effects of the intellectual inertia and skepticism of the ordinary man of science upon many of the exuberant, freewheeling, and sometimes less useful ideas of the great or near great. Finally, the sum total of the less important research endeavors of the very large number of mediocre scientists is tremendous and probably accounts for most of science as measured by both input of energy and output of results. It is amazing how little of this is realized by most people outside of the sciences. Again we become aware of an intensely human situation. Science is like that.

4 · SCIENCE AS COMMUNITY

Now to take a further step, we should note that the enterprise of science is not only human and social, but communal in a deep sense that transcends that of a local community or town. There definitely is a "science community," a term one hears with increasing frequency these days, and it has the usual attributes of human communities. It is a group of likeminded people with similar interests, predilections, goals, modes of thought, intellectual equipment, training and experience. A group of likeminded people become a community as it develops a common way of life and work, a language of its own as well as other means of communication, group ideals, ethical and moral codes, sanctions, institutions and organizations, patterns of responsibility and authority, a collective style of thought, customs, orthodoxies, and so on. As all others, this community is affected by the usual vagaries, adequacies and shortcomings of human beings. It has its politics, its pulling and hauling, its pressure groups; its differing schools of thought, its divisions and schisms; its personal loyalties and animosities, jealousies and hatreds, and rallying cries; its fads and fashions.

A community is then not a mere collection of likeminded people who are individualists that have been thrown together more or less by chance. No, it is a highly cohesive group bound together not only by *similar* purposes but by a unique *common* purpose, and by a spirit and faith that express their solidarity, by their *common* interests and needs, by feelings of interdependence, by mutual understandings that can come about only through the common life and work. And so it is with the science community—and even more so with the several individual science communities. All this is very hard to describe, though nonetheless real. There is something intimate about it, something shared and deeply felt, though unspoken. It can be understood truly only within the community.

An interesting question arises here: How do physicists, say, recognize each other as belonging to the physics community? I suggest that they do this not by appealing to precise definition and analysis, but rather by *smell,* so to speak; on the basis of feelings, and the vague, unspoken, intimate, indescribable, but deeply felt intangibles of common interest, purpose, and attitude that become compellingly real to those who participate in the shared experience and life of the physics community.

This is no mere insipid, useless sentimentality. It is utterly realistic and practical. How, by way of a single illustration, does an editorial board of a physics journal proceed when a paper of high quality is submitted for publication, which they think deals with chemistry rather than physics and should appear in a chemistry journal? Does their judgment result from the conscious, logical application of formal definitions or criteria? By no means. While, to be sure, they may give some thought to more formal considerations, their decision rests basically on translogical and undefined feelings, on insights, intuitions, and a sense of values they have developed for the most part unconsciously, as with other physicists they have gone about the business of physics.

It is to this kind of intuitive thinking and feeling that many physicists resort when they are called upon to say what is physics, or what is the difference between physics and chemistry. They find the conventional definitions to be quite inadequate. Many a long, animated, informal discussion of the subject—even formal committee deliberation—has yielded the profound conclusion that physics is what physicists do when they do physics, and that physics is what goes on in the physics building, and chemistry what goes on in the chemistry building of a university. To be a physicist is to "go in for" physics. From the viewpoint of pure logic this is admittedly an empty definition, and a circular one at that. But operationally, i.e., in terms of what happens in the actual life of the physics community, it is rich with meaning, and by means of it physicists are able to answer many practical questions and make important professional decisions. Moreover, the same remarks apply also to other scientists, chemists and biologists, indeed to the science community in general.

While the sketch of science that is developing is still far from complete, its main features are I trust beginning to appear. What is emerging is the picture of a science that is the common interest and intellectual passion, the common work and life, the common faith and structure of beliefs, of a closely knit, mutually dependent, dynamic community of likeminded, dedicated people called scientists.

This concept of the community is of crucial importance for a thorough understanding of the nature of science. Many of the actualities of science, such as we have studied, seem paradoxical or even absurd when viewed from the perspectives of the idealized stereotype of science. When seen in the light of this communal concept, however, they become understandable and appear altogether natural. In arriving at this idea we have reached an important milestone or vantage point. It provides us with a powerful unifying idea for everything to be said hereafter, and everything that has been said thus far. Now let us consider its significance for an understanding of religion.[4]

5 · RELIGION ALSO IS COMMUNAL

In developing this subject we shall not need to go into as many details, because to a surprising extent science and religion are alike in their communal aspects, and much of what has been said about the one applies equally to the other. Actually we have already appealed repeatedly to the community concept for the interpretation of certain aspects of religion. All we need therefore is a somewhat more explicit treatment of it. To begin with, there certainly exist a Jewish community and a Christian community, and each of them has its own history and characteristic way of life. They are very human communities, conditioned by the ordinary characteristics and frailties of human beings. As for the Christian community, the fact that it is bound together by religious concerns and loyalties has not prevented the appearance within it of unsavory politics, with its pulling and hauling, and its pressure groups; of controversies, jealousies and hatreds; as well as rallying cries. It too is in many respects heterogeneous, including the greater and the lesser, those with vision and those without it, the open-minded and the closed, the cantankerous and the gentle, the conservatives and the liberals, the tolerant and intolerant, the informed and uninformed. Among them there are different views about the nature and methodology of religion—and of Christianity. And yet in a very real sense it is a fellowship of like-minded people with a common faith, purpose and goal, among whom there have evolved many common ideals, standards and mores, a characteristic style of thought, customs, orthodoxies and so on. This community has developed a language and literature of its own, as well as a body of beliefs and practices that are truly meaningful, and that really matter to it.

An obvious aspect of this community is the amount of doctrinal disagreement that has developed in its midst, disagreements that have caused serious ruptures and estrangements, and altogether too often actual bloodshed. But even so, what is just as obvious to one within the community is the remarkable degree of understanding and communality among its members. Thus virtually all Christians share the basic beliefs expressed by, say, the *Statement of*

Faith. Denominations differ on many details, but fundamentally they agree that Jesus Christ is their Lord, that in Him God came among men, that He came because God the Father so loved the world that He gave His only begotten Son, that He was crucified, dead and buried, that He was resurrected, and so on. They all believe in and practice worship and prayer. It is this common faith, belief and practice, this common experience with God and man, that is the basis for what has come to be called the "fellowship of the saints." What this term stands for is hard to explain, and is nearly ineffable. And yet, as was said relative to the spirit or feeling of fellowship in the science community, there is something intimate about it, something shared and deeply felt, though unspoken; a feeling of solidarity in spite of doctrinal independence. This can be understood fully only from within the community. How does one Christian recognize another? I suggest that in the last analysis he does this not by doctrinal definition or analysis, but rather by the indescribable but deeply felt intangibles of the common faith and life that become so compellingly real in the shared experience and thought of the community. Nor is this mere sentimentality any more than in the case of the science community.

Having said all this we must now take cognizance of some significant differences with regard to the communality of science and of religion. One of these is that both the communal experience itself and the idea of it have played very unequal roles in the two communities. In the consciousness of scientists the concept of community has been peripheral and is still emerging, while in religion it is not only central, but has been so for a long time. No doubt one reason for this is that science has not been communal for more than approximately two hundred years. Before that every man was for himself, so to speak. A scientist, to use his modern cognomen, was typically an amateur natural philosopher, as he was called then, for whom the pursuit of scientific knowledge was a side line, a hobby for his spare time. If he was fortunate, he knew a few others like himself and corresponded with them sporadically. Not till the science academies and societies were established in the seventeenth century were there opportunities for scientists to get together formally at meetings. Not till then did they have a chance to publish their ideas and findings in so-called *periodicals* rather than in books of their own. Only then did a community of science begin to evolve self-consciously. Even then science did not become a profession in the modern sense until less than a hundred years ago. It is a fact also, I think, that the idea of a community as I have defined it has not played an important role in the thought of science until recently. Even today many scientists would probably not think of it as being important to a real understanding of science.

In religious thought, on the contrary, the idea of a community has been in the forefront for a long time. Certainly this is so in the Judaeo-Christian tradition. Thus we have the concepts of "the people" and of "peoplehood" that have been so central and determinative in Jewish thought and life. Without this concept we could not understand Judaism at all, either ancient or modern. In Christianity the corresponding idea is that of the Church, conceived not primarily as an ecclesiastical organization, but as a community of people who have a history of significant common, revelatory experience, who have a faith and body of insights that bind them together in a common life and work. Both Judaism and Christianity have been at once personal and communal. Both have fiercely defended the sanctity of the individual, even if not always consistently, and yet the Jew has regarded his personal destiny as being bound up indissolubly with that of his people, and so has the Christian.

No doubt the primary reason for the prominence of communal self-consciousness in the Judaeo-Christian tradition is that its fundamental concerns are so deeply personal. Thus ultimate concern has to do with love of God *and of neighbor*. Faith is an intensely personal trusting. And basic religious belief is belief that matters most personally, e.g., that God is a father-God, that He forgives, and so on. It is with regard to personal concerns, in contrast to more impersonal ones, that the need for fellowship and community, and for a sharing of faith and belief, becomes especially pressing— even though there may not always be a strong conscious awareness of it. Even so a religious community does not appear on the scene fully developed. It takes time. Certainly it did in the case of the Jewish community. In an important sense the Old Testament is

an account of how "God's people" as a community came into being gradually—and perilously, for at times it almost dissolved.
Similarly the Christian fellowship became a community in its fullest sense, i.e., in all its important manifestations, only gradually.
Certainly it seems to have required about two or three centuries
before it became a well *organized* community.

There is still another feature that distinguishes Judaeo-Christian
communality. Over and above the sense of personal values and
concerns there is the sense of a distinctive *communal* mission, and
a sense of *communal* responsibility to God. This is the significance
of such phrases as "the people of God" and "the holy (catholic)
Church." The meaning of the word "holy" in this connection is
"set apart for God," for holy purposes. Both Jew and Christian
feel that their community came into being through the will of God.
They remember the call that came to Abraham to leave his home
and country to become the father of a people through whom all
other peoples should be blessed. This was a "chosen" people,
chosen not to be the recipients of "special advantages and favors"
from God, but to be sufferers, sufferers for the redemption of the
world. This, I believe, is the Jewish interpretation of that powerfully suggestive and meaningful expression the "suffering servant."
For the discerning Jew the Exodus means that God freed his people
from Egyptian bondage not merely to enjoy a new land of milk and
honey, but to carry out the communal "suffering servant" mission.

6 · THE CHURCH

Similarly, the Christian thinks of his community as God's people, brought into being by the will of God for a particular purpose.
Now the communal embodiment of Christianity is the Church, and
just as Christianity as a faith or religion is badly misunderstood,
so is the Church. Some of the misunderstandings of it, for which
it is itself partly responsible, we have already dealt with. We must
now consider others; and frankly in the attempt to explain lucidly
I shall illustrate my points by reference to the science community.

The first suggestion is that the Church be thought of *fundamentally* as a *"fellowship* of the saints," not as an institution. Now

saints are people who realize that they are sinners with no moral or religious superiority, who yet own Jesus Christ as their Lord and together share his living presence among them, and who are saints (sanctus: holy) in the sense of having been "set aside" for God's purposes, by His will and their own acquiescent choice. The Church is this fellowship, the instrument of God for the achievement of His purposes in history, for the spreading abroad of love of God and love of man, for redemptive action through love and suffering.

To be a member of *this* Church does not mean that one's name must necessarily be on the membership roll of a congregation or denomination, though for most Christians this does seem important. What it does mean primarily is membership in the sense of common loyalty, commitment and faith, of the truly communal spirit and unity—with all that this implies. An understanding of this will clear up much that may otherwise seem puzzling or even unreasonable.

Consider for instance the assertion that only in the Church can men find "faith *unto salvation.*" What is the meaning of this claim? Well, I should say that it is equivalent to the assertion that a one-man physics is impossible. Religion, while it is highly individual, is not solitary, but inescapably social. Since it has no method of achieving truth inerrantly, it insists on cross-checks and mutual validation to eliminate, or at least minimize, error and hallucination. It is not true that religion is subjective, *whereas* science is objective. Both want objectivity. Neither achieves it perfectly. Insofar as they do achieve it, it is through intersubjective testability, i.e., both insist that before the experiences or findings of an individual are accepted as valid they must be communicable and make sense to the community.

In certain quarters religion has been conceived primarily in terms of certain so-called psychological phenomena, "religious experiences" such as glossolalia ("speaking with tongues"), ecstatic enthusiasm, visions and trances, voices, "prophecy," alleged miraculous encounters, certain kinds of mystical experience and extrasensory perception and the like. From this point of view religion is simply subjective, intensely and ineffably private, essentially incommunicable—and anything but objective. As we shall see later, it is not this kind of thing that is meant by Christianity, or Christian faith or "Christian experience."

That there have been such psychological phenomena in the Church cannot be denied. But they have been suspect, and certainly they have not played a central role in either the thought or experience of the Church. In fact very early in the life of the Christian community it was pointed out that such phenomena are virtually meaningless and worthless, especially by St. Paul in his discussion of glossolalia, which he considered to be unintelligible babbling that did not contribute to understanding.

What the Church has always treasured most are those experiences that can be shared, concerning which one can speak and reason, through which it claims to have come to know divine reality—objectively. When members of the Church recite, say, the *Statement of Faith,* they are testifying not only to what they have experienced individually and privately, but to what they know others have experienced also, and they know this by having cross-checked with others. That God is a loving father is not a private, solitary insight, but one that has been validated communally. While in religion there is no intersubjective testability in the sense of precise control experimentation by which one subject can cross-check with another, there certainly is intersubjective testing in the sense that one's own experiences and observations are compared with and thus tested against those of other subjects. It is because they have not met this test that many reports of visions, miracles and other "religious experiences" by solitary individuals have been regarded as spurious, and have been repudiated by the Church. In neither science nor the Church is objectivity possible for the solitary individual. It is achievable only in community.

Moreover, it is from the community that the individual gets his techniques and methods, and learns to make these as effective and objective as possible. In science the way a graduate student learns to do research is by example and contagion, i.e., by watching and working with more experienced workers. Similarly, he *inherits* from them the scientific faith, attitude and spirit. He does not generate these himself *de novo.* Thus it is only within the community that science can be learned in the richness of its fullest meaning. Even the partial knowledge and understanding of non-scientists is mediated to them through the community. There is nothing arbitrary about all this. It is simply that the nature of life and of the learning process are such that science can be learned and experienced adequately only in this way. And so it is with the Christian faith.

It is often asserted also that the divine revelation occurs only among "God's people" or within the "community of faith." Admittedly this also sounds rather arbitrary and exclusive in a snobbish sense. But can it mean anything more—or less—than to say that revelatory insight about nature can come only to those who by virtue of their attitude toward, and understanding of, nature are prepared to receive it, namely those who constitute the community of scientific faith? Thus disclosure of the universality of gravitation could come to Sir Isaac Newton only because he already knew something about gravitation. Likewise the disclosure of Jesus Christ as Son of God who was given by the God-Father because He so loved the world, could occur only within the community that "knew God" in a sense that made this disclosure meaningful.

Then there is the implication of this relative to the atheist. Does it mean, it is often asked, that since he is not a member of the Church God cannot ever be disclosed to him? If this is to be taken seriously an adequate answer would require that more be said than would be appropriate for present purposes. Suffice it to remark then, first, that many so-called or self-styled atheists are no more than rebels against the traditional concepts of God, or against institutionalized religion, or particular conventionally formulated beliefs of the Church, not against the "God beyond the gods," or the genuine *community of faith.* When Nietzsche cried out "God is dead," this was not actually an atheistic cry, but a profoundly discerning protest against the conventional god image of his time that had become largely emptied of actual meaning and potency. Such men are not men without ultimate concern, and they are not necessarily outside of the community in faith and spirit. Second, if a man *actually* were an atheist, i.e., knew nothing whatsoever about *God* either experientially or theoretically, either by choice or otherwise, I don't see how there could be divine revelation for him, any more than there could be scientific revelation for him who has absolutely no knowledge of nature. Clearly we are now on shaky, problematic ground. Does there actually exist anywhere a man so completely isolated as that? Is there anywhere a genuine a-theist or a-naturist? I do not know.

7 · INSTITUTIONAL ASPECTS OF COMMUNITY

We must now consider explicitly the institutional aspect of community. Many persons object to religion mainly because of its institutional manifestations. Religion may be all right, they say, but not so the Church. Why must there be a Church? Again the answer follows from the nature of community. History seems to reveal a sort of natural law that communities must in time become organized and institutionalized, or they disintegrate. This seems to be so even though paradoxically the process of institutionalization itself contains the seed of disintegration.

The pattern of the evolution of a community like the science community seems apparent. First there are likeminded individuals here and there who are attracted to one another in small groups. Then these coalesce into larger informal fellowships. Very soon thereafter the need arises for some sort of organization for the purpose of expediting communication in various ways. As the fellowship becomes more conscious of goals to be achieved and of tasks to be undertaken, more organization is needed; officers are given authority to act for the group; constitutional provision and safeguards are established; budgetary questions arise; membership becomes formalized; codes and canons appear; publications come into being; liaison is established with other communities and with government agencies; and so on. All this has happened with respect to science, and in this way a science community has come into being, and is becoming more and more institutionalized.

Of course all this has happened also in the evolution of the Church, though, since it came into being much longer ago, the process of institutionalization has progressed much further. It may be that the only reason why the science community as we know it today is not as highly organized as the Church is that it has not been in existence nearly as long. Time will tell.

Now another thing that is evident from history is that organizations can become vested interests, become vicious, and obstruct progress and growth. There can be no more convincing evidence of this than that furnished by the history of the Church. Indeed so convincing and well known is it that I need not go into detail about the sorry business. There is much to be ashamed of in that history. And yet there is also much to be proud of, and in part this is because the Church is not only a fellowship but a structured institution that can bring to bear on the performance of its tasks various devices that make for efficiency and that become available only through organization and planning. It certainly makes sense to say that there are very undesirable features of the institutional Church—as there are of institutional or organized government, business, education, medicine, and labor. It does not make sense to say that there should not be organizations and institutions. Who would want to say that science would be better off if it were not organized at all, and who could say in all honesty that the Church would be?

8 · ENVIRONMENTAL ASPECTS OF COMMUNITY

The last thing to be pointed out in this connection is that communities are in the world and that they are profoundly affected by their cultural environment. Contrary to prevalent opinion, science has not risen above its environment by becoming independent of or immune to external influences or pressures. It has interacted with its environment with momentous effects, and often its own reactions have been conscious and deliberate. The same is true of religion. Moreover, communities exist side by side with others. Often they interpenetrate one another. No one community lives unto itself. For a particular individual this means that he always belongs to two or more communities. Life and mankind being what they are, this inevitably means tension and perplexity, often conflict of faiths and loyalties, or ideals and purposes. It also means in most cases that there are helpful interactions and stimulation among communities and their members. This is another reason for not regarding science and religion in too narrow or separatistic a manner.[5]

9 · NOT AN ARGUMENT BY ANALOGY

At this point I should like to re-emphasize that in developing the theme of the human, social and communal nature of science and religion I have not meant to build up an argument or proof by analogy. It is *not* proposed that because science has certain characteristics therefore religion should have them also—or vice versa. There have been elaborate attempts to develop just such an argument and to construct a "scientific religion" or theology.[6] In my opinion these are misguided, just as would be attempts to construct a "scientific art" or "religious science." It may well be that the religion and science communities can learn from each other, and that each can study the other "scientifically," but that is quite another matter. At any rate the intent here is not to exploit analogies in the ordinary sense, but simply to make a factual study of the nature of science and of religion; and thus far the study has shown that both are communal, and that an understanding of this will clear up many misconceptions of their nature—and of their relations.

There is an aspect of the religious community that is especially abhorrent to many people, namely its theology. Religion, they say, may not be so bad, but theology definitely is. An acquaintance once said, "I don't mind reading a book on religion once in a while, but I would not touch one on theology with the proverbial ten-foot pole." Here, it is thought, is where most of the troubles come from that are symbolized by the cliché "science versus religion." I want to consider this in the next chapter in connection with a study of the three main components of the life and work of science and religion.

CHAPTER V

The Threefold and Circular Nature of Science and Religion

With Special Reference to Theory

1 · ABOUT THEOLOGY

Whenever we discuss the relations between science and religion we are sure to encounter the troublesome word *theology*. Many people react to it just as they do to the words *creed* and *revelation*. They think of it as a boring and irrelevant enterprise in verbal hair splitting, as the attempt to dogmatize in the worst possible sense and to rationalize and perpetuate fossilized ideas and prejudices. They regard the truth claims of theology as preposterous. Perhaps they have read about warfare not only between science and religion, but more specifically between science and theology,[1] and have concluded that it is theology that has caused all the troubles in this area.

Now, again I plead for a different point of view. True, theology can be boring, irrelevant and intolerant. But it can also be exciting and adventurous, mightily relevant, utterly open-minded and tolerant. While at times it has split logical hairs needlessly, it has also been genuinely sensitive and creatively discriminating. Some of the greatest minds of our time are working in theology. And not a few others who are not theologians have discovered it to be a rather fascinating subject and enterprise. Moreover, its relations with science have by no means always been antagonistic.[2] As often as not theology has been an ally.

The misconceptions and prejudices to which I have referred are due to a large extent to a lack of understanding of what theology is and does, and how it is related to religion, as well as to ignorance of what the actual, rather than alleged, teachings of theology are.

Unfortunately, it is not too easy to find out what theology really is. While *in practice* theologians seem to agree rather well on what it is and what it means to theologize, when it comes to giving formal definitions and stating explicitly how it operates, they do not. The situation seems no different from science. In their talk about science scientists don't agree either. Albert Einstein is credited with having said that if one wants to know what science is one should not listen to what scientists say about it, but go and watch them at work. Apparently this can be said about theologians also. Therefore we shall proceed not by citing explicit definitions of theology, such as appear in its literature,[3] but by describing its function and its processes as an enterprise of the community of the faith.

Theology is the conceptualizing, interpreting, explaining, theoretical part or aspect of religion.* It builds structures of thought or conceptual systems in response to men's desire and need for understanding and meaning. It explores the implications of revelation and faith in the realm of belief as well as that of actual life and existence. It is that activity of religion that uses formal logic and rules of evidence, and subjects creedal claims to the critical analysis of reason. It endeavors also to translate the expressive, symbolic language of faith into the discursive, precise language of the disciplines, and vice versa.

Theology is therefore important business—quite indispensable. We could not get along without it any more in religion than we could dispense with theoretical physics in physics. Its role in religion corresponds in many, though not all, respects to that of theoretical physics, which is the symbolizing, system-building part of physics.

To elucidate the role of *theory* in relation to other aspects of science and religion I should like to present a diagram—and apply it first to science.

---

* Theology is here regarded as internal, not external, to religion. This is one of the standard ways of looking at it.

2 · SCIENCE IS THREEFOLD AND CIRCULAR

Science may be regarded as being threefold in nature and activity, as suggested by the three circles of Fig. 2. First (circle *a*), it is *empirically descriptive,* engaging in data gathering by observation and experimentation. Second (circle *b*), it is *theoretical,* producing symbolic structures or systems for purposes of correlation of concepts, generalization, explanation and prediction. Third

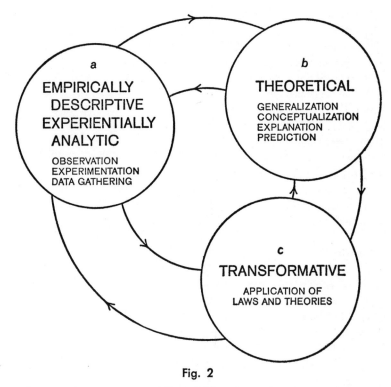

Fig. 2

Schematic Representation of Threefold and Circular Nature of Science and Religion (circle *c*), it is *transformative,** transforming man's natural and cultural environment by so-called "practical applications" of scientific laws and theories. None of these terms is completely adequate or accurate in its connotations. To give concrete meaning to them let us look at some examples.

Consider the physics of gases. The part of it that provides information about the experimentally known behavior of gases is represented by circle *a*. Much of this information is formulated in the so-called gas laws, such as Boyle's Law and Charles' Law. These *laws* are expressed in mathematical equations which indicate how various measurable physical quantities are related to each other, and how they vary (change) together under different physical conditions. Thus Boyle's Law tells us approximately how the pressure of a confined gas varies with its volume, while the temperature is constant. Charles' Law shows how the volume and corresponding temperature vary while the pressure is held constant. The General Gas Law relates all three variables, i.e., the pressure, volume, and temperature, while the mass is constant. Such laws are useful in that they correlate and represent huge amounts of data. They provide information about both what has actually been observed, and what may be expected under specified conditions, i.e., for particular values of the pertinent variables.

Now physicists, like other scientists, are the kind of people who are not satisfied with having a lot of data about specific properties of gases, or even isolated laws that correlate data. What they want also is a way of correlating the laws so as to get an over-all view of the behavior of gases. Moreover, what they want especially is a mathematical structure, or theory, from which to deduce the various known gas laws and predict the existence of others not yet known. Physicists feel that when they have provided such a theoretical structure they have *explained* both the data and the laws. It is this theorizing that is represented by circle *b*.

In building such theoretical structures the physicist often proceeds by imagining, i.e., hypothesizing, a "model" which he invests with certain postulated properties. He then works out a mathematical description (system of equations) of how the imagined

---

* For this term I am indebted to my colleague Professor Paul D. Krynine, distinguished mineralogist and able philosopher of science.

model works. If from this mathematical system he can deduce the laws he wants to correlate, and it meets certain other criteria of acceptability, he has a satisfactory theory.

In the case of gases, a remarkably successful theory is the so-called Kinetic Theory, which pictures a gas as consisting of a huge number of molecules that are extremely small relative to the distances between them, that are in random motion, that maintain the pressure of the gas upon the containing walls through their impact upon them. Not only does this theory "explain" the gas laws per se, but it sheds light on the laws of thermodynamics, the more general science of heat.

Circle *c* stands for the application of the empirical information about gases and the theory of gases to particular concrete situations for the purpose of controlling or transforming the physical world. There is a vast body of gas technology, which at least in its modern manifestations is to a large extent the direct consequence of this threefold activity of the physics of gases.

Another example. Chemistry is empirical and directly descriptive (circle *a*) when it propounds the laws of chemical reactions in terms of observed, measured quantities, such as weights and volumes and combining proportions, and of empirically specifiable classes or species of substances, such as elements and compounds, or gases, liquids and solids. A case in point is the so-called Law of Lavoisier, which tells us that when a chemical reaction takes place in an enclosure no weight, or mass, is lost or gained in the process. This means that in the case of a chemical decomposition the sum of the weights of the resulting components equals the weight of the sample decomposed. Thus if water is decomposed the sum of the weights of the components hydrogen and oxygen equals the weight of the water decomposed.

This is a much more meaningful and empirically useful statement than the more general one that is often called the Principle of Conservation of "Matter." This is because the term *matter* used in the latter is itself not a quantitative term, and one cannot therefore properly speak of measuring the amount of it in a container. On the other hand it is clear what it means to measure its mass or weight. Actually, like all the empirical laws of science, this Law of Lavoisier is valid only approximately, since the weights before and after a chemical reaction never do in fact add up exactly. There is always at least a small "remainder," and this may be due either to "errors" in measurement, or, say, to the presence of another, but unsuspected, component. When we take this into account we can see that in the laboratory this law, if taken precisely, functions not as a description of an aspect of nature, but as a method, an investigative tool, for the discovery of unknowns. Therefore from this point of view it could be stated more explicitly as follows: "If in the course of a change we discover a decrease in the sum of the masses of the bodies enclosed in a container, we shall say that a body having a mass of exactly the difference between the two measured masses has gone from the container in which the change took place. We shall look for this fugitive body." [4] Many a new chemical substance has been found this way. Now it is this kind of thinking that is symbolized by circle *a*.

Of course, the experimental situation with regard to chemical reactions cannot be described completely without recourse also to other laws, such as the Law of Proust, or the Law of Definite Proportions, and the Law of Dalton, or of Multiple Proportions. These are also formulated in terms of measurable quantities such as weight or mass, and of empirically identifiable chemical substances. Here we are still in circle *a*.

Now we enter circle *b*. The experimental laws of chemical reactions—and others—are correlated and explained by the grand and remarkably successful theoretical structure called the atomic and molecular theory, which *postulates* some entities called molecules, atoms, electrons and so on and assigns to them certain properties. The growth and developments of this potent theory provide one of the most interesting and informative chapters in the history of ideas, and illustrate many features of the evolution and nature of scientific theory in general.

Chemistry is one of the sciences that illustrate most obviously the transformative activity of circle *c*. It has become not only analytical and exploratory, but truly creative. It has not only studied many substances already in existence, but has produced many new ones, such as the novel plastics, to take only one example. It has profoundly affected our mode of life and physical environment in other ways—witness its contributions in the fields of nutrition and medicine.

There was a time when science was thought to include only circles *a* and *b*, its empirical and theoretical aspects, while *c* was regarded as engineering or technology—i.e., not "really" science at all. Today this is no longer the case. Many members of, say, the American Physical Society and American Chemical Society are engaged mainly in applying their sciences to technological problems, and yet consider themselves to be physicists or chemists, not engineers. It is becoming more and more difficult to distinguish between so-called "pure" and "applied" science.

The three components of science are, of course, inseparable and utterly interdependent. Each is meaningful only in relation to the others and to the whole. This is symbolized in the diagram by the circular arcs with arrows. Each circle is connected with each of the others by two such arcs, pointing in opposite directions to indicate action-and-reaction effects and feed-back relations. Those between circles *a* and *b* signify respectively the facts that, on the one hand, theory depends upon and comes out of observation and experimentation, and, on the other hand, observation and experimentation at their best are influenced, and often even guided, by theory. A theoretical structure endeavors to correlate and explain what one has seen. But what one sees is often affected or even determined to a considerable extent by the theoretical viewing screen through which one does the observing. Moreover, what one sets out to look for in the first place is often determined by what theory has led one to expect. We have here another case of circularity. Still another is depicted by the double connection between circle *b* and circle *c*. Theory is important in assaying the possibility of particular useful applications and indicates the direction they might well take. Conversely, theory is enlarged and enriched as one struggles with new problems in the attempt to apply it usefully. Circles *a* and *c* are similarly connected, signifying that observation and experiment often suggest or open up possibilities for useful applications without the mediation of theory; and conversely, technological needs and developments call for or suggest new areas for data gathering. The point of all this is that science is an indivisible unity. It thrives best when all three of its main components are thriving, and when there is a proper balance and interdependence among them. And for present purposes it should be stressed especially that science would be inconceivable without theory.

Although in its essentials this threefold sketch depicts the nature of all the basic sciences, there are significant differences of emphasis among them. Physics and astronomy are alike in their strong emphasis upon mathematical theory—and in their quest for the grand, all inclusive theory. But, for astronomy, circle *a* represents almost exclusively only observation and measurement, with virtually no experimentation. After all, astronomers cannot experiment with the planets or stars, i.e., intervene in their courses to manipulate them under control conditions. Nor is astronomy outstandingly transformative. Useful applications are very few indeed, and they are confined mostly to determining time and place (latitude and longitude). As we review the physical sciences, passing from physics and astronomy, through chemistry to meteorology, geology, mineralogy, and physical geography we find progressively less emphasis on precise measurements, controlled experimentation, and mathematical theory. In the biological and social sciences this trend persists and becomes even more pronounced. Moreover, the various particular science communities appear to have somewhat different viewpoints about the nature of science; that is to say, their philosophies of science are not all alike. Not only does this show up in different methodologies, but in different conceptions of basic purposes. Thus physical scientists lean more toward positivistic conceptions of theory, emphasizing their symbolic nature and predictive purpose, while the biologists seem to tend toward more realistic views about theory, regarding them as being more pictorially descriptive of nature itself.

It is therefore not too meaningful to speak of a "typical" science. They are all different in significant respects. Moreover, it is unsafe to generalize as to scientific methodology. Thus it is not true that experimentation is what characterizes all sciences. Nor do all of them think predominantly in quantitative terms.

With respect to all the sciences, however, the three circles of our diagram have this historical significance: that they represent different phases of their development. In their first stage the purely experiential, i.e., direct observation and simple data gathering, predominates. Only later do the more analytical and critical, interpretive and transformative activities put in their appearance. No doubt this is inevitable.

3 · THE THREEFOLD AND CIRCULAR NATURE OF RELIGION

Turning now to religion, in many respects it also is portrayed rather well by the diagram. Certainly it too is threefold, with *a* the experiential or empirical component, *b* the theoretical or explanatory and interpretive one, and *c* the one that is transformative and pragmatic, or what is sometimes referred to as "applied religion" or "practical religion." * Here also we encounter the feedback interactions and circularities indicated by the dual connections between the component circles.

Theology is represented by circle *b*. It interprets and explains the faith experience of the religious community and is, therefore, largely determined by it as indicated by the arrow from *a* to *b*. On the other hand, by the concepts, doctrines and thought patterns theology develops, it profoundly affects, and partly determines, the religious life of the community (arrow from *b* to *a*). Moreover, both the life of faith and the enterprise of theology profoundly affect the transformative action of religion in the realm of ethics and morals, and in social action, while it in turn deeply affects them (opposite arrows). In a sense, then, theology (circle *b*) has a dual stance and purpose. Facing circle *a* it conceptualizes, interprets, criticizes and reacts upon the revelatory experience of the community of faith. Facing circle *c* it elaborates the implications of faith and belief for life and work, and points to the responsibilities and problems of the community in the transformation of the world.

* It should be noted that I am not now using some of the terms in the diagram, e.g., *experimental* and *data gathering*. This indicates that science and religion are not parallel in all respects relative to the diagram. There *are* significant differences.

4 · EXCURSUS ON EXPERIENCE

Since all this must seem rather abstract and vague, I shall presently try to give it more concrete meaning by applying it specifically to Christianity. Before doing this, however, I must explain my usage of another troublesome word, namely *experience,* and its correlate, *religious experience.* First, I disavow completely the meaning often ascribed to "religious experience," namely, the emotional and ecstatic kind of experience often referred to as "getting religion," or "old time religion." I disavow also that usage, fashionable among certain schools of philosophers and scientists, that would restrict its meaning to only those of its aspects that are associated with physiological and instrumental perception.

What I *do* mean by it coincides more nearly with its common-sense meaning: it is what happens to people, is imposed upon them by the realities of existence. It is neither conjured up by the imagination, nor created by postulation. It is *given.* I mean what most people mean when they say: "I *experienced* the horrors of war; I did not merely read about them." "This teacher understands children through experience, not merely theoretically." "One must experience worship and prayer to be able truly to appreciate and understand their meaning and power."

My usage does not deviate far from that of contemporary empiricism, which recognizes that experience involves the whole of a man in his relation to all of his "environment." It is a broad and inclusive term. There are many kinds of experience, e.g., seeing the stars, hearing the thunder, becoming aware of the beauty of the rainbow or the beauty of holiness, falling from a ladder or falling in love, finding faith. One may experience "separation from man and God," being "born again," the revelatory disclosure of the universality of gravitation, or of the fatherhood of God. Experience includes what happens to communities as well as individuals. Moreover, experience has a variety of aspects or dimensions. Consider, for instance, how much may be implied when someone says, "Last week end we visited Niagara Falls. It was an experience never to be forgotten." What is there about such an experience that is never to be forgotten? For many people at least this: the overwhelming impression of tremendous physical force, energy and power; the aesthetic impact of indescribable beauty and grandeur; and, for some, the sense of awe emanating from the awareness of the God (however conceived) behind it all.

So rich in content is human experience that no one discipline or intellectual endeavor is able to comprehend it in its entirety. Each one is forced to deal with it only partially, in only a restricted number of its many facets. The sciences attend to aspects of reality that can be experienced through instrumental observation and experimentation. Yet each science provides a unique kind of experience. The various arts are interested in other facets of existence, those not discernible or measurable by instruments. Again each leads to a different kind of experience. All of these are equally genuine and valid, even though they are in many respects different. *Experience* is therefore another word whose full meaning cannot be stated by intensive definition, but can be communicated only ostensively or contextually.

I disavow also the intention of assigning to experience the role attributed to it by exponents of what has been called the "religion of experience." According to this school of thought, theology is related to experience as physics is related to light and electricity. If this were true, experience itself would be the source of religion, and theology a branch of psychology or anthropology. As I see it, however, experience is the gateway to, or the transmitting mediator of, the reality experienced. The physicist experiences light and electricity. What he attempts to do is conceptualize and correlate the data of that experience in order to achieve knowledge or understanding of light and electricity. What should then be said is that experience plays the same role in religion as it does in physics. This means that theology is related to experience *as theoretical physics is related to experience.* Theological theories are to the data of the religious *experience of God and man* as physical theories are to the data of *experience of light and electricity.* From this standpoint religion, including theology, is no more a branch of psychology or anthropology than is physics, including theoretical physics.

5 · CHRISTIANITY

Now let us elucidate these generalities by considering how they apply to Christianity regarded as a religion. There are those who would deny the legitimacy of this, on the ground that Christianity is not a "religion" and can, therefore, not serve as a proper example. Whether or not it should be so designated is, of course, a matter of definition, and we should not now become involved in a dispute over definitions. It seems clear that Christianity *is* a way of life, a faith, ultimate concern, *agape,* and a demand calling for commitment of all of oneself to love of God and love of neighbor. If religion is this sort of thing, Christianity is religion. It seems equally clear that Christianity *is not* a system of specified doctrine and ritualistic practice that is required of its devotees. If by "religion" is meant such a specific and specified system, then Christianity is not a religion. He whom Christians call their Lord bequeathed or enjoined no such system. What the early Christian Church carried abroad was the Gospel, news, *good news* about something that had happened—not a system of formal code.

In any case, whether Christianity should be conceived as a religion or not, let us speak of it as the way of life, faith and thought of the Christian community, in the sense that physics is the way of life, faith and thought of the physics community; and let us see whether the threefold diagram adequately symbolizes its nature at least in part.

First let us consider its experiential, empirical aspects (circle *a*). What seems to have astonished the pagan world most when it was invaded by early Christianity was not a new philosophy or novel system of ritual, but the way the early Christians loved one another, their neighbors, their enemies, and their God. And what a God! A God who loved men, who ruled by love and self-sacrifice rather than by arbitrary, monarchical and punitive power, and who was like one Jesus of Nazareth, a young Jew whom they experienced as the Christ. The lives of these peculiar, loving people were centered in and revolved around this Christ. Everything they talked about—be it nature, man or God, life or death, the past, present or the hereafter—had become and remained meaningful to them because of Him. No wonder they were nicknamed *Christ-ians*. What seemed especially odd was the fact that this Jesus was not a great celebrity. He had been known only in a very small region of the Roman empire, in Palestine. He had been in the public eye and had made his impact upon his companions and contemporaries only a very short time, not more than three or four years. After that he had been denounced and executed as a criminal. And yet these Christ-ians claimed that after His death this Jesus came back to life. Then to cap it all, they claimed that after He left them again, this time by "ascending to heaven," something tremendous happened to them that they described by saying that the Spirit of the Master, "the Holy Spirit," had descended upon them, and that thereafter this Christ had remained real to them. And finally millions of Christ-ians since then have believed all this and have testified that for them, too, Christ was—and still is—in some sense utterly alive and real.

In studying and recounting this we are operating in circle *a,* the descriptive, empirical and fact-finding part of the intellectual enterprise of the Church. To carry out this work involves various disciplines, and a variety of scholars who must be scientifically expert just as are the investigators of the history and phenomenology of the life and thought of any other community or people. Thus Old and New Testament studies require experts in the history and languages of the Near East and in textual analysis and criticism. Other disciplines involved in this empirical study of Christianity are Church history, anthropology, psychology and sociology of religion, comparative religion, comparative literature, and still others.

When Christians go forth to propagate their faith, what they are trying to do then is to share the to-them-remarkable, precious experience and way of life described in circle *a.* It is a fact of history, however, that deeply moving experience and faith always eventuate sooner or later in linguistic and theoretical expression. This is true in both science and religion. If it is an abiding, ongoing religious experience, i.e., an experience involving all of a man and touching upon his ultimate concerns, it also finds ritualistic expression. If it affects all of a man, his mind as well as his heart, inevitably it will surely be analyzed, and reasoned about. It will call forth questions and demand explanation and interpretation. It is in response to these primal demands for communication, linguistic expression, the sanctions of reason, and these urges to analyze, question and evaluate, that Christian theology (circle *b*) has come into being.

What Christian theology endeavors to *interpret* is this Christian way of life and faith, this God-man experience of the Christ-ian community and individual. The facts or data it deals with "theoretically" are those of that experience. This basing of theology upon the body of Christian experience is indicated in the diagram by the arc-arrow from *a* to *b*. The critical function of theology, its demand that the Christian experience make sense and be under control, in short, its reaction upon experience, is indicated by the arrow from *b* to *a*.

Out of this interplay and interaction of basic experience and of critical, analytic, interpretive reflection upon it have come many conceptions of God, the world and man, that together constitute the theological doctrines of Christianity. There have been many theoretical systems, just as there have in science. Some have weathered the storms of life and others have not.

The early Christians had inherited a monotheistic conception of God from Judaism. In the light of their Christ experience this conception was immeasurably enriched. The heavenly father image took on new meaning because of the tremendously revealing Christ experience. Both His love and wrath took on new meanings, in the marvelous light of Christ's love. Sin became even more terrible in its enormity in view of the crucifixion on the one hand, and of the enriched conception of love and God on the other. The concepts of death and of the "principalities and powers of darkness in heavenly places" were transformed by the experience of the resurrection. The understanding of the nature of man and the world could never again be the same *after* the Christ experience as it had been *before*. To give all these new insights formal expression has been the task of theology.

In this connection attention is called to a series of theological treatises that exemplify with distinction the role of theology relative to the experience of the Church. It is the "Library of Constructive Theology." [5] Some of its volumes are entitled *God in Christian*

Thought and Experience, The Christian Experience of Forgiveness, The Christian Experience of the Holy Spirit, Redemption and Revelation, The World and God, The Christian Society, The Relevance of Christianity, Worship. The first three of these titles in particular are directly suggestive not only of the purpose, method and spirit of the series, but of the fact that Christianity is fundamentally empirical rather than philosophical, and that a basic function of theology is to interpret the experience of faith and by reaction upon it to help shape it.

An important aspect of theology's function has been to interpret the significance of Christian insights for succeeding generations, for different cultures, and for different situations. In so doing it asks what the situation really is in a given time and culture, relative to man's relation to God and existence. It asks what it means in practice, in that situation, to love God and one's neighbor, and what action is called for, and what duties thus devolve upon Christians in the world of affairs and in personal relations. This brings us to the relation of Christian theology to the transformative aspect of religion, symbolized by the dual connection between circles *b* and *c*. This function of theology is at least as important as the other. Here theology must analyze the ills besetting mankind, and its grave concerns and anxieties, both those that are universal and those that appear in particular situations. It must also be conscious of the great questions man asks, that reflect his ultimate concerns—for to love man significantly in the *agape* sense, one must be aware of his longings and predicaments. But more than that, theology asks which of man's questions are truly meaningful and of ultimate concern and which are not in the light of the Gospel, and what light the Gospel can shed upon the situation.

It is probably correct to say that, relative to the transformative function of religion, for a long time the primary concern of Christianity was the "salvation" of the individual "soul." Now by *salvation* I do not mean "being saved from eternal damnation and hell fire" in the once popular sense, but from the domination of sin, man's lower, egocentric self, and from the social and cosmic forces that are beyond his control and yet threaten his very existence and being. While the contemporary Church would certainly not discount the importance of personal salvation, it is preoccupied much more than formerly with the salvation of man in community and therefore with the problems of society at large. And theology has contributed in no small measure to the development of this wider point of view, and to the channeling of Christian action along appropriate lines (circle *c*).

There is probably no better exemplification of this social concern of theology than that of Reinhold Niebuhr. He has struggled mightily with the problems and terrible dilemmas facing the person who would love his fellow men in a real world. As Gordon Harland has put it, "He has sought to clarify the insights and resources of Christian faith in such a way that they may be savingly related to the structures, dynamics and decisions of large social groups. . . . His whole work serves the one concern—to relate redemptively Christian faith and social responsibility, *agape* and the struggle for social justice." [6]

Much of the work of the Church that is indicated by circle *c* might aptly be called Christian technology. Under this heading come such activities as the improvement of man's physical environment and the acquisition of the necessities of life, proper food, clothing and shelter; the conquest of disease, ignorance, superstition, slavery, and tyranny; the support of efforts toward peace and the abolishing of war; the establishment of justice and fair practices in business affairs, in labor and management relations; the improvement of race relations; the support of good government. Home and foreign missions in their various aspects come under this heading, as do many other activities. In all these fields the Church has developed experts, among both its clergy and laity, who may well be regarded as the technologists of the Church for the transformation of the world. Parenthetically it should be remarked that much of this application of the gospel to real life needs to be effected within the Church itself. I refer to unjust social practices and other evils that are condoned or even engaged in by large sections of its membership, as well as to practices of the institutional Church itself. There is much to be done here.

It must be recognized, of course, that much of the Church's labor of love in the world is done by unsophisticated Christians with an intense love of neighbor, who are quite uninformed theologically. It might then be said that for them transformative, social action springs directly from the basic Christian faith and the sense of responsibility to God and man. This is why circle *c* is connected to both *a* and *b*. To put this into the faith language of the community, our love-action relative to our fellow men (circle *c*) is determined largely by our experience of God and man (circle *a*) and our theological beliefs about them (circle *b*). Also, conversely, our religious experience and theological conceptions are very much affected by our actions among men.

Now a few remarks about certain approaches in theology. The need to relate the insights of the Christian faith to the ultimate questions and concerns of man is the basis for a theological method developed by Paul Tillich, which he calls the "method of correlation." "It correlates questions and answers, situation and message, human existence and divine manifestation." [7] A somewhat similar method is employed by Walter M. Horton.[8] It is built around basic perennial questions and concerns, and universal human needs, and presents answers that Christianity has to offer. Some of the problems discussed by him in this way are: the universal outreach toward some sort of deity, the universal problem of religious knowledge, the question as to whether cosmology presents a religious problem, the universal need for fellowship and inspiration, the universal need for hope, and so on. An especially valuable feature of his method is to present different theological points of view within Christianity, Roman Catholic and Protestant, conservative and liberal, and with regard to each important subject, to indicate the extent of consensus as well as disagreement among Christians.

A critical perusal of the writings of the large majority of present-day theologians will reveal them to be remarkably open-minded and far from sectarian or denominational. It should be understood more widely than it is that theology is not primarily a set, or sets, of beliefs or doctrines, but a process by which such doctrines are developed. It is no doubt true that Baptists, Lutherans, Methodists, and Presbyterians differ typically in regard to certain doctrines. There are historical reasons for this. But it makes no sense to talk of Baptist, Methodist or Episcopalian theologies as such. I believe it to be true of the vast majority of theologians of today, that when they theologize they do this without conscious commitment in advance to any particular sectarian position or conclusion. My observation of theologians at work, as well as my reading in the literature of theology, has convinced me that contemporary theology does not differ significantly from science in its open-minded commitment to the free and unhampered quest for truth and insight.

6 · MORE ABOUT CIRCULARITY

Several cases of circularity have been pointed out by means of the diagram. By *circularity* of thought I mean a relationship between ideas that are so utterly interdependent that each presupposes the others and yet none is the necessary logical foundation of the others. By circularity of experience I mean a similar relationship between components of experience.

A case in point is the relationship existing in science between experiment and theory (circles *a* and *b*). Which *must* come first? Which is logically the foundation or prerequisite for the other? Should a student who is entering upon the study of a given subject, study theory first and then make experiments, or vice versa? There has been many an argument about this among scientists and they inevitably end in a stalemate. Probably there is no answer. Perhaps they are the wrong questions—like the hoary one about the chicken and the egg. The fact is that some people do—and they should—start with theory, and others with observation. This is true not only in the student laboratory, but also in the research laboratory, not only among beginners, but also among experts. There is neither logical nor psychological or pedagogical priority that must govern all cases in these matters. In the diagram this is signified by the oppositely directed arcs connecting circles *a* and *b*. Other such circularities have been pointed out.

There is circularity also with respect to the interaction of experience and thought, and therefore to the entire enterprise of science, involving all three circles. Together the latter constitute the "scientific circle." This means first, as pointed out earlier, that science is an indissoluble tri-unity, each of the three components (circles) depending on the others, and none being the logical prerequisite of the others. It means also that experientially one can

enter the circle anywhere and then proceed around it in either direction—as suggested by the opposite arrows. Thus some scientists
have in fact been drawn into the large circle by the fascinations of
certain phenomena (circle *a*), others by an elegant theory (*b*),
still others by useful technological problems (*c*). Some introductory physics courses begin with beautiful demonstrations to be observed and explained, others with an aesthetically appealing theory
which suggests experiments to perform, and still others with a steam
engine or a musical instrument to be taken apart and analyzed both
experimentally and theoretically. Again we are confronted by evidence of the essentially non-logical and intensely human character of the scientific enterprise.

Likewise in religion. As already noted, there are the various
circularities apparent within the diagram. These are illustrated by
the manner in which religious experience and doctrine influence
each other. But there is over-all circularity also, with complete
interdependence of all three of the component circles, none being
the prerequisite foundation for the others. Some people enter this
"religious circle" through the gate of belief, others by experience,
still others through social action. There are also, of course, other
points or modes of entry. None is logically prior to the others.
Once in the circle, a person may then proceed around it in either
direction as his insights and experience grow.

Why belabor this matter of circularity? First, simply to portray
the true nature of science and of religion, which are both much
misunderstood in this regard. Second, there are methodological
and philosophical implications. Some scholars would make of
science—and of religion—a logical "system," depicting it not as
a three-ring circle, but as a three-sectioned vertical column. At the
bottom there is an allegedly impregnable a-priori, presuppositional
foundation, from which confidence in the reliability and authenticity
of the whole structure derives. Upon this rests logically a two-story
column of the empirical and theoretical, and on top of this the pragmatic or applied. In some schemes the order of the empirical and
theoretical is reversed.

As I see it, all such attempts to build systems are misguided.
Neither science nor religion (or theology) can adequately be represented by them. They are not reducible or dissectible into de-

finable entities that can be put together into philosophical or logical systems. Moreover, history seems to show convincingly that systems built upon a-priori, metaphysical foundations are built on shifting sands. Science and religion *are* non-logically circular in experience and thought, rather than logically columnar. In this respect they are remarkably similar, so much so that if we understand and appreciate the nature of the one, it will help us to understand the other. There are, of course, vast differences between them, as we have already noted. But these are not the kind that would appear in a discussion of basic structures or over-all patterns of purpose, such as our diagrams depict. Thus it is not true that the one deals with observable experience and the other does not; that one theorizes and the other does not; that one is socially applicable while the other is not. Where they differ is in the *kind* and *content* of the experiences they represent, in the kind and object of their speculations and theories, and in the kind of practical, transformative action they undertake in the world.

7 · OVERLAPPING ACTIVITIES AND IDEAS

We have emphasized that the three components of science, and religion, are not independent, but continually interact, as symbolized by curved arrows connecting the circles in the diagram. We must now recognize that in the lives of both the individual and the community these activities are usually not only interrelated and interdependent, but that they actually overlap. To depict this graphically we might in our imagination change the three-ring diagram by enlarging the circles so they overlap. This would suggest that any given investigation or development often falls in one of the areas of overlap and is rarely purely empirical, or theoretical, or even transformative. Almost always it makes contributions in more than one area.

Specialization in a science like physics or chemistry has developed to the point where many physicists and chemists regard themselves as either experimentalists or theorists. This separation has gone so far that many a theorist seems utterly at a loss when confronted with apparatus or tools; and many an experimentalist when confronted by a serious theoretical problem calls in a theorist as consultant. For this and other reasons it makes sense to think of the experimental and theoretical—as well as transformative—activities of science as significantly and identifiably different and separate, while yet realizing that they overlap, thus making it impossible to draw sharp boundary lines between them. This is not unlike the situation in religion. There too are specialists, the professional theorists (theologians) and the practitioners; though there is the same overlapping of thought and activity as in the science enterprise.

Therefore, whenever we herein use the terms *experimental, empirical* or *experiential,* and *theoretical, interpretive* or *theological,* and *technological, pragmatic* or *transformative,* it is to be understood that overlapping and fuzzy boundaries are taken for granted. If this is kept in mind we can avoid many circumlocutions and awkward qualifying phrases and sentences with respect to these terms.

CHAPTER VI

The Permanent and Transient
in Science and Religion

Truth and Certainty

1 · THE PROBLEM—RELATIVE TO SCIENCE

Why have we spent so much time on the human, communal and non-logical aspects of science and religion? Because this is crucial to an adequate understanding of the kinds of experience, knowledge and insight they represent, the methodologies they have developed, their spirit, purposes and goals, and, of course, their strengths and weaknesses. All of these have characteristics that derive directly from the fact that, broadly conceived, they are in actuality intensely personal and communal.

There now arises an important question which will be considered first with respect to science. Can a typically human enterprise, and a veritable three-ring circus * or three-fold circular process such as science, possibly yield reliable knowledge? And does it? Can we reasonably claim to be able in this way to achieve certainty about anything truly important? Are we not simply fooling ourselves? This question becomes even more pointed when we remember that it is asserted frequently these days that science yields only probabilities rather than certainties, that it has destroyed all absolutes, and that therefore knowledge can only be relative—whatever that may mean. Aside from this alleged uncertainty and relativity, scientific knowledge is also said to suffer from lack of sta-

* For those who have not lost their love of this remarkable American institution, the circus, it is by no means a derogatory characterization of science to call it a three-ring circus.

bility and permanence. What was "known" a hundred years ago, or even only twenty-five years ago, is said to have become obsolete and been displaced by something more recent. What we think we "know" today will therefore suffer the same fate tomorrow. Probably every science teacher who has taught more than only a few years has repeatedly heard former students say rather wistfully: "I suppose if I were to take your course again now I would find everything to have changed. Nothing would be at all familiar. Science moves so rapidly that everything I learned must now be out of date."

There are, however, some elements of inconsistency or paradox in the views many people have on this subject. For one thing, they may assert that in science ideas are in a continual state of flux and replacement, and at the same time believe that "the scientific method" necessarily yields inerrant truth. For another, they may point with pride to the continual turnover of scientific knowledge, feeling that it indicates that in science ideas are not allowed to become fixed and fossilized "as they are in theology," and yet believe that only in science can one find solid, objective, and undeniable truth—which if it had these attributes should never need replacement. Clearly the question of the permanence or transience of scientific knowledge and understanding is not unimportant and needs to be looked into.

Before going into this I suggest that while these paradoxical beliefs indicate that people have confused ideas on the subject, they may nevertheless indicate also that they have some fundamentally sound, important understandings of science. Though perhaps more instinctive than reasoned, they may mirror not only perceptive discernment of fact, but also a keen sense of what ought to be. Don't we all feel that science *should* give us reliable, permanent knowledge, and yet that it *should* also keep an open mind about that knowledge and be ready to change it at any time this seems indicated? And shouldn't this be so also in religion? How can we reconcile these seemingly contradictory demands? And how do the actualities of the scientific and religious enterprises correspond to them?

I am not proposing to enter upon a metaphysical discussion of certainty or permanence, but rather an operational one, endeavoring to discover their empirical meaning in life, and right now especially in the life, work and thought of the science community.

2 · PERMANENCE AND CERTAINTY

That science does in fact offer permanent and certain knowledge is illustrated by the statements listed in Table I.

Let us consider first the eighteen statements comprising part A of the Table. No doubt everybody will grant that they are accepted as true *today*. But do they represent *certain* and *permanent* knowledge? In what sense? Dodging for the present the meaning of the term "knowledge," they represent the kinds of assertions that the experience of the science community has shown do not require replacement, and that succeeding generations of scientists accept as the foundation for further work. They are conceded to represent actuality and fact about which there exists no doubt among scientists. If anyone were to question their certainty, it would have to be at the level of metaphysical abstraction or the kind of reasoning that leads to solipsism. Any basic doubt about them would be tantamount to doubting that any communicable knowledge is possible. But this is not the kind of thinking scientists engage in as scientists. For them these are facts, because they have been ascertained by methods they regard as reliable, and been confirmed many times in many different ways. Scientists have "bet on them" —by assuming their reliability as they have planned and carried out a great variety of scientific and technological operations—and have won.

Nor is there a question here of probability versus certainty. In the actual empirical situation they are treated as certainties. To assert that these statements represent *only* a very high degree of probability rather than certainty would be to make an operationally, or empirically, meaningless and unverifiable assertion—or at best to give unusual meanings to these terms, which would for present purposes be nonsense.

All the examples considered so far represent more or less isolated facts. As I have suggested earlier, however, while such separate facts are of tremendous significance, and their discovery has often required an enormous amount of painstaking work, the sci-

TABLE I

Items of Scientific Knowledge Regarded As Permanent And Certain

A. Separate Facts

1. Microscopic inspection has revealed that tissue, such as onion skin, has a characteristic cell structure.
2. Tissues differ in cell structure.
3. A leaf has mouthlike cell structures in the epidermis, called stomata, that play a role in the "breathing" of the plant.
4. There are variable stars, whose brightness changes periodically.
5. A certain class of variable stars, cepheids, have a particular, characteristic, predictable type of variation.
6. There are optically invisible stellar bodies, whose existence is indicated by "radio waves" rather than "light waves."
7. When bodies vibrate rapidly in air they thereby produce pressure waves in the air.
8. When such waves impinge upon a human ear under certain circumstances there is produced the sensation of sound.
9. Sound echoes are the consequence of the reflection of such pressure, or sound, waves from surfaces such as walls or mountain sides.
10. The loudness of a tone is determined primarily but not exclusively by the intensity of the sound wave.
11. The pitch of a tone is determined in the main by the wave frequency.
12. The loudness of a tone is determined in part by the wave frequency.
13. There is a gas, hydrogen, with the following physical properties. . . .
14. There is a gas, oxygen, with the following physical properties. . . .
15. Water consists of hydrogen and oxygen.
16. Some diseases are caused by bacteria.
17. Some diseases are caused by viruses.
18. Radium emits three kinds of rays called. . . .

B. Relational Facts, Factual Relationships

19. For a specimen of gas having a given mass, the product of the pressure and volume, divided by the absolute temperature is a value that remains approximately constant for limited ranges of the variables. (This is the general gas law.)
20. The motions of virtually all moving objects encountered in every-day life can be described and predicted to a very high degree of accuracy by a system of mathematical equations expressing Newton's Laws of Motion.
21. The propagation of sound waves of low intensity can be described to a high degree of accuracy by the mathematical equations of waves of infinitesimal amplitude.
22. The chemical elements when arranged in order of atomic weight (or preferably atomic number) show a periodicity of chemical and physical properties.

ence community is never satisfied until it has found ways of relating various particular facts by means of more comprehensive generalizations. Some of these, too, represent certainty and permanence. These may be called *relational facts* or *factual relations*. Most of the experimentally derived so-called *laws of nature* or *laws of science* * come under that category.

Part B of the Table presents a few examples of such relational generalizations. Item 19 is a scientific law, actually a combination of several discrete laws. Item 20 is not expressed in the form of a law but comprehends several. So does item 21. It reveals the functional relationships of the variables encountered in the study of ordinary pressure waves and implies correctly that if we work with intensities of higher orders of magnitudes other equations must be used. This item covers a large body of fact. The last one, the twenty-second, is different from the others. It cannot be called a law of nature in the usual sense. Rather it is a diagrammatic scheme (the Periodic Table) for presenting a large body of knowledge in such a way as to reveal significant relationships.

Now while it may not be as immediately obvious to the general reader, these items from Part B of our list represent permanence and certainty quite as much as do those of Part A. About all of them it can be said that successive generations of scientists have been able to accept and build upon them, and that the science community expects never to have to unlearn or relinquish them—unless indeed the natural world itself changes in time.

Quite clearly then it is not true that in science *everything* becomes outdated and has to be abandoned sooner or later. There are at least some things, and they are actually vast in number, that science offers, which can be accepted with complete confidence.

3 · TRANSIENCE

It is not difficult to find equally convincing evidence of transience. See for instance Table II. Admittedly this list is rather a hodgepodge of ideas chosen more or less at random. But every-

---

* One of the most unfortunate inadvertences in the history of science and of thought was the application of the term *law* to such generalizations, since these do not *pre*scribe for nature, but only *de*scribe how we find nature to operate.

TABLE II

Abandoned Scientific Ideas

1. The solar system is geo-centric.
2. The motions of planets can be described best mathematically by the Ptolemaic system of cycles and epicycles.
3. The geometry of stellar physical space is Euclidian.
4. The stars influence people's lives and the course of empire.
5. The Earth is flat.
6. The Earth is a few thousand years old.
7. Heavy objects necessarily fall faster than lighter ones.
8. An object can move only while it is propelled by a force.
9. The total amount of mass in the universe is constant. (Mass cannot be transmitted into energy.)
10. There exists a subtle fluid called caloric.
11. Nature abhors a vacuum.
12. There is a substance, plogiston, with the following properties. . . .
13. Biological species are immutable.
14. Some organisms may be accounted for by spontaneous generation.
15. Water and air are simple, elementary, indestructible and unalterable substances.
16. Atoms are indivisible and indestructible.

one of them was at one time or another widely regarded by scientists as an important component of scientific knowledge. Today no jury of scientists would accept any of them. It is argued sometimes that scientific ideas are never abandoned completely, but rather only modified, amplified or transformed gradually into others. However that may be—and much can be said in support of such a thesis—the fact is that there have been many that were quite acceptable in the past that the science community rejects utterly now, whatever their history may have been in the meantime. The items on our list are only a few of the many that might have been cited as examples.

There is only one item on which I would expect any serious challenge, namely the fourth on the list. Obviously this was a doctrine of astrology. It will be argued therefore that it represented not a scientific view, but only superstition. But this would be too hasty a conclusion. Mark Graubard in his book, *Astrology and Alchemy, Two Fossil Sciences*,[1] has presented much evidence in support of the thesis that both astrology and alchemy were once respectable sciences by the best criteria current in their day.

The basic doctrine of astrology, embodied in item 4, was believed to be true by the vast majority of the scientists at that time
—and believed for what they regarded as scientific reasons. If
Graubard's thesis is correct, and I find it convincing, not only does
science experience change by the elimination of particular beliefs
or teachings, but by the disappearance of entire individual sciences,
such as astrology and alchemy.

4 · TWO STREAMS IN THE HISTORY OF SCIENCE

How can one identify and distinguish between the permanent
and impermanent, the certain and uncertain in science? Where
should we expect change to come in the future, and where not?
What can we depend on? What should we be prepared to relinquish, and what not?

The answer is, I think, a rather simple—though profound—one.
We need only remind ourselves of certain features of our three-fold
diagram. Physicists, to take them as typical of scientists in general,
operate at two different levels or in two different areas, first that
of the concrete, tangible world (circle a) with its intricate vacuum
systems, its metal bars or wires, electric switches, calorimeters,
magnets, noises, measuring instruments, cyclotrons, and transis-
tors, and, second, that of an abstract, imaginatively constructed
world (circle b) which has at various times been inhabited by
postulated entities such as the Ptolemaic cycles, epicycles, and
crystalline spheres, the luminiferous aether, caloric, phlogiston,
the various mechanistic models, the Bohr atom and now the mathematical models of quantum mechanics. While, as I have said earlier, the kinds of thinking that are representative at these two levels
continually interact and can therefore not be separated sharply,
they are nevertheless significantly different and represent in the
history of physics two parallel—though not independent—processes of growth and development, two streams of ideas. The one
is in the main empirical and factual and the other predominantly
theoretical and interpretive. An analysis of the two lists will show
that their items belong respectively to the first and second streams,
the factual and the interpretive.

To identify further these two streams in the history of science and to clarify the difference between them let me present a brief historical sketch of the science of optics, the physics of light. To begin with, what do we mean by light? Or what has the word "light" meant historically? How has our knowledge of it grown?

Today we frequently begin a study of optics by pointing out that the word *light* has two basic meanings. It refers, first, to the sensation of light, that which goes on in the eye and brain that enables us to see, and second, to that physical agent which when it impinges on the eye causes the sensation of sight. The former is the business of the physiologist and psychologist and the latter that of the physicist. No doubt for a long time in the dim past there was no thought of an agent or entity called light. There was simply the prescientific experience of lightness and darkness, day and night, the sun, moon and stars, luminous bodies such as fires, fireflies, lightning and later candles, as well as illuminated objects that could be seen in the presence of luminous bodies. There were also the colors—of rainbows, sunsets, flowers and butterflies. Also associated with lightness was warmth since many luminous bodies supplied appreciable heat. Then there was the reflective mirror effect of water surfaces and ice, and the refractive bending effect when a straight branch was stuck into the water and appeared broken at the surface. These are primitive experiences shared by all men.

The *science* of light (optics) was born when these experiences became more sophisticated, when the first critical observations and experiments were made to discover what system or order there might be in all this welter of apparently unconnected phenomena, and when somebody began to use his imagination and asked how these things can be, how they might be explained. It must have been at that time when people began to think of light as some-*thing,* a stuff, an influence, an entity that can in some sense have separate existence, that comes from somewhere and passes through space to impinge on things, including eyes. The science of optics developed thereafter out of two kinds of questions and concerns. First, just how does this entity that came to be called "light," behave, i.e., by what laws can its behavior be described? Second, what must be the nature of this light? What properties can it be *imagined* to have that would account for its known behavior?

In answer to the first question, physics has in the course of time identified an impressive series of optical phenomena, which it has described by means of quantitative laws, such as those of rectilinear propagation, reflection, refraction, dispersion, interference, diffraction and polarization; emission and absorption; velocity, and still others. Moreover, the empirical meaning of the word *light* has been extended to include what has often been called "invisible light," to which the human eye is not sensitive. Here we have infrared and ultraviolet light, as well as X rays, gamma rays, radio and radar waves, all together referred to as electromagnetic radiation.

Parallel with this empirical development there has been an equally interesting and impressive theoretical development—in response to the second type of scientific question, namely what hypothetical properties the entity light might * have that could account for its behavior. The question here is how we may think of light imaginatively; what properties we can imagine it to have.

When but little was known about light only a very simple interpretation was required. To "explain" simply the primitive experience of the lightness of day and the darkness of night, light was thought of as something that was let loose upon the earth from the heaven above at dawn and then withdrawn at dusk to be stored overhead somewhere at night. When the body of known phenomena became somewhat more extensive, a more sophisticated explanation was constructed, namely that the eye sends out rays that act somewhat as feelers by which things can be seen. An alternative explanation was that both the eye and the object seen emit something the "mixture" of which resulted in vision. Aristotle considered that light was not a material substance at all, but the quality or action of a medium called the "pellucid." These theories seemed more or less adequate as long as the known facts about light were in the main qualitative. When, however, Snell formulated the law of refraction quantitatively, and Roemer determined the velocity of light, the old interpretations seemed no longer adequate. At about that time two rival theories were advanced, the corpuscular emission theory by Newton and the wave theory by Huyghens. These were radically different in conception. The one, Newton's, postulated that luminous bodies emitted light particles which moved in straight lines

* Notice, not *must* have.

at enormous velocities. The other, Huyghens', postulated that light was emitted and propagated as waves. Both "explained" rather satisfactorily most of the laws of optics then known, namely the laws of rectilinear propagation, reflection, and refraction, and the fact of the velocity of light. For quite some time for various reasons the corpuscular theory was preferred. Then, when the phenomena of interference and diffraction became better known, the wave theory seemed to offer more adequate explanation. Thereafter for a while these light waves were thought of as mechanical waves in a luminiferous medium postulated as an elastic solid (aether) with rather unique characteristics. At first these waves were regarded as longitudinal. Later, when polarization was discovered, they were postulated to be transverse. Still later the waves were thought of as electromagnetic in nature, i.e., they were not waves at all in the usual mechanical sense (of something actually waving to and fro), but rather periodic variations in an electric and magnetic field.

This brings us to approximately the beginning of the twentieth century. At that time there appeared new experimental knowledge that the old theories could no longer handle adequately, e.g., some of the facts of so-called black body radiation, and then the photoelectric effect. These led first to the quantum concept and then to what was essentially a corpuscular conception. This was very disconcerting at the time because it seemed like a return to Newtonian ideas which had been abandoned long since. It was especially disconcerting, however, because the particle concept seemed adequate for only some of the phenomena of light, while for others the wave conception remained more useful. With this paradoxical situation we end our historical sketch.

It is quite evident from this look at the second component of the history of optics, that of its theories, that a characteristic feature of it is impermanence. This is altogether typical of theoretical science in general. A particular theory holds sway only temporarily, and may then be drastically modified or even abandoned. The situation with regard to the empirical stream is certainly different. There change is mainly by addition or refinement. Once an experimental finding has been accepted by the physics community, i.e., once the frontier or pioneering stage of its inception has been passed, it remains permanent—with rare exceptions. To summarize, what the community has experienced and accepted as objectively factual remains so. What it has created imaginatively in the attempt to explain and interpret is always subject to change.

Before proceeding to the next subject I want once more to disavow any intent of separating the empirical and theoretical streams sharply. They are recognizably different but not completely separate. Nor are Tables I and II identifiable respectively as purely factual and theoretical. This would be an oversimplification. I made no such claim. And yet the items of those tables respectively are also recognizably empirical and interpretive—remembering the caveat entered at the end of the preceding chapter.

5 · NO BARE FACTS IN SCIENCE

Two terms have been used rather casually thus far, namely *fact* and *factual*. Their meaning needs now to be sharpened up. Facts are commonly thought of as simple units of knowledge that result from pure perception, i.e., perception unadulterated by conceptual or interpretive intrusions. As far as scientific facts are concerned this is a misconception. It may be, though I doubt it, that at the level of common experience so-called facts are occasionally ascertained by "pure, direct perception," i.e., by simply opening one's eyes and looking—just plain looking; but in science this is never the case. Always "scientific seeing" is more than mere staring or gazing. It requires, and in fact always is accompanied by, some selecting, discriminating, abstracting, conceptualizing, correlating and interpretational cerebration. This is certainly true of the gathering of so-called *raw* data, the spots one sees or pointer readings one makes. This requires that one isolate certain factors or variables for specific observation or measurement, thus declaring others to be unimportant or irrelevant for the particular purpose of the moment. One must carefully specify any significant constants and their values.

One must make the observation or measurement in such a way as not significantly to change the very values one is trying to determine. If one tried for example to determine the temperature of a small drop of cold water with a large warm thermometer, the water would immediately become warmer. Therefore the temperature registered finally would not be the original low one that was to be measured. This requires the selection of appropriate instruments and techniques. One must be conscious of "errors" and proceed in such a way as to minimize them, or at least be able to specify the range of their magnitudes. Not infrequently one must decide which data should be thrown out. And finally one must draw conclusions from a set of data, and often this means choosing between alternatives that may at the time seem equally valid.

Throughout this process of data gathering, which consists of making decisions, and then "looking," and then deciding again, one is necessarily guided or influenced consciously or unconsciously by theoretical considerations. In the case of some data the purely perceptive element predominates, while the conceptual-theoretic elements play only a minor role. In others the emphasis is reversed.

Now when we talk about scientific *facts,* as distinguished from mere *data,* these remarks are even more to the point. By a *fact* of science I mean an important, rather extensive item of knowledge which in general represents a conclusion from the analysis and interpretation of a considerable body of data. Interpreters of science often create the impression that typically its facts are simple items of knowledge that are directly perceptible, e.g., the hardness of a rock, the number of petals of a flower, the colors in the rainbow, the temperature of an object. When it is asserted, however, that science puts a premium on *facts* rather than on guesses or on credulous beliefs, surely this refers to something more significant than such pre-scientific trifles, or to isolated raw data, namely to the kind of hard-won units of knowledge that are listed in Table I.

In the discovery of such facts the interplay of observation and experimentation with theory is even more evident than in the case of the gathering of raw data. Furthermore, this often becomes clearly apparent in the language used for reporting the facts. As an example consider the statement: The speed of light is 186,000 miles per second. In the first place, this number is not a raw datum, i.e., one immediately perceived or directly measured. It is the result of elaborate *indirect* thought and measurement. When in the seventeenth century the Danish astronomer Roemer "measured" the speed of light,[2] what he saw directly was a series of appearances and disappearances, i.e., eclipses, of the satellites of Jupiter. The timings of these gave him his raw data. Surrounding and inter-penetrating the whole enterprise of obtaining and processing the data was the rather sophisticated thought that light is something moving in space with finite, though huge, speed. This profoundly affected everything he did, including the way he stated his con-clusions.

When somewhat later Bradley studied the aberration of light and concluded something about its velocity, the data he dealt with were not the times of eclipses of satellites, but the apparently para-doxical positions of the stars (parallax) and their systematic vari-ations during the year. But by that time the idea of light moving with a finite, rather than infinite, velocity seemed less strange; and, as is evident from his own account of his work, it saturated his thinking and his expository language. With Fizeau, Foucault, Michelson and others, who achieved more and more accurate measurements, the idea became progressively more "self-evident," so that now it constitutes a part of the presuppositional founda-tion of thought structures and habits upon which all thinking about light is built.[3] Today we find it almost impossible to think of light in any other way than as a very rapidly moving entity—even *though there may actually not be anything moving at all.* When, for instance, it is reported that a certain kind of glass has an index of refraction of say 1.5, this is interpreted as the ratio of two ve-locities of light, that outside of the glass and that inside—though the raw data are very far removed from any direct perception of an actual motion. Thus the statement of fact about the index of refraction is expressed in terms of a theoretical interpretation that has for practical purposes assumed the role of a "self-evident" pre-supposition.

Not only does this presupposition function as the foundation of thinking in optics, but in other sciences as well, e.g., astronomy. Consider an assertion such as this: There are many spiral nebulae hundreds of millions of light years away. Probably all astronomers would call this a factual statement. And yet it is far from being a *bare* fact. Basic to it is the assumption of the finite speed of light, as well as others, e.g., that this speed is the same everywhere in stellar space, and is the same now as millions of years ago. I am, of course, not calling these assumptions into question. But I *am* saying that they are there as presuppositions in the thinking of the astronomer, though he seems rarely to point them out. Factual statements of astronomy are then laden with presuppositions. Some of them come out of earlier empirical findings, others from particular theories, and still others from basic ways of conceiving the universe—such as, that its fundamental physical properties and laws are uniform throughout all space and unchangeable in time.

When a geologist asserts that a given mountain range is older than another, he expects this to be accepted, I believe, as a factual statement, as also, when he "explains" what happened in the very dim past to form certain valleys, or to produce certain deposits. And yet he would no doubt readily admit that both his data and factual conclusions are heavy with conceptual and theoretical elements. For one thing, throughout his investigations and studies his thinking is conditioned by the assumption, hidden or otherwise, that the basic cause-and-effect relations that are known now were operative also millions of years ago, that in this respect there has been no evolutionary change since then. For another, many of his assertions of fact represent conclusions drawn at least in part from particular theories that, because they have been very successful, have taken on the status of a-priori, or virtually self-evident, assumptions. Therefore such facts must be regarded as partly interpreted, rather than bare, raw facts.

One more point on this subject. Not only are all important scientific facts inevitably interpretive, because they necessarily result from theoretical and presuppositional considerations, as well as from purely analytical-statistical data processing, but their acceptance by the science community frequently depends more on the former than on the latter. This means that when a choice must be made between two competing conclusions, the decision may be determined not by the compelling persuasiveness of the observed data, but by the even more compelling demand that they fit satisfactorily into prevailing theoretical thought structures. Therefore it happens not infrequently that large bodies of data are disregarded or rejected because no interpretation has been found by which they can be correlated meaningfully with other bodies of data or with accepted theories.

Let us consider two historical episodes that illustrate this. Several years ago the physics fraternity was confronted by conflicting claims of two extremely able experimentalists, Millikan [4] at the University of Chicago, and Ehrenhaft at the University of Vienna. The former asserted on the basis of his well-known oil drop experiments that the electron, defined in terms of a certain quantity of electric charge, is the smallest observable quantum of negative electricity. Ehrenhaft, on the other hand, maintained, on the basis of other ingenious * experiments, that there are observable subelectrons, i.e., submultiples of Millikan's electrons. Since it will be impossible to go into the details of how this controversy was resolved, let me simply say that Millikan's claim prevailed, because his interpretation, on the basis of theoretical considerations and of an over-all view of other relevant findings in the field, was superior.†

Somewhat later another important case of conflicting claims confronted the physics community, this time with respect to the celebrated Michelson-Morley experiment. According to traditional concepts prevalent prior to the Einstein era, the measured speed of light, when its motion and that of the earth are parallel, should be different from that obtained when the motions are perpendicular to each other. For various reasons it was important at the time to be able to test this expectation experimentally. If the existence of this predicted difference could be confirmed, it would further establish prevailing conceptions of light; if not, new and more adequate ones would be called for. The Michelson-Morley experiment was designed as a "crucial experiment" to measure this expected difference.[5] When Michelson and Morley performed the experiment (actually a series of them) they interpreted their results as being negative. They felt that the difference yielded by the analysis of their data was not statistically significant, and therefore that the predicted difference was not found. This is one of the most im-

---

* I have heard Millikan say in a graduate course that Ehrenhaft was an extremely clever experimentalist and that his subelectron work was very ingenious.

† I am indebted to Professor Philipp Frank for first calling my attention some years ago to the fact that the choice between the Millikan and Ehrenhaft claims *could not* be, and in fact was not, determined by the analysis of the experimental results themselves. For details, see Millikan, *Electrons, Protons, Photons, Neutrons and Cosmic Rays.*

portant, pivotal findings in the history of science. Some years later D. C. Miller, who had had serious misgivings about the Michelson-Morley conclusions, repeated the experiment with what he considered to be improved procedures and equipment. A vast amount of data was obtained. From these Miller concluded that he had found a significant, positive difference (between the parallel and perpendicular velocities) and announced his conclusions as contradictory to those of Michelson and Morley. He, like his distinguished predecessors, was an extremely able experimentalist. At that time there was no evidence of significant systematic errors in his work. And yet his conclusions failed of acceptance by physicists, and the reason was clear. They were at variance with a large body of accepted fact and theory. They defied interpretation along lines that would have made them consistent with prevailing thought structures. Clearly, then, apparently impeccable experimental adequacy does not suffice to force acceptance of experimental findings, or to establish factuality. *Factual statements are interpretations as well as summaries of observed findings.*

It is of course obvious that there is a difficulty here arising out of an apparent contradiction. On the one hand I urge that facts are permanent, whereas interpretations are not, and on the other hand that facts are in part interpretational. How can anything, in this case a fact, be permanent if a part or aspect of it, in this case its theoretical component, changes? In trying to resolve this let us appeal to an analogy. There is a sense in which a building may be said to be permanent even though the color of its stonework may be changing, or internal alterations may be made in it from time to time. An institution, say a university, that has existed for a thousand years may in this sense be regarded as a permanent feature of its culture even though in some respects its structure or its personnel may have changed. In this sense the fact that water consists of hydrogen and oxygen may be said to be permanent even though the theoretical content of the words *water, hydrogen* and *oxygen* may be altered from time to time. It is a permanent fact that living tissue has cell structure, even though, I understand, the theoretical content of the term *cell* has changed considerably since its inception. In this sense it is also a permanent fact that one finds the Boyle's Law relationship (or a more inclusive one) in the laboratory, even though the kinetic theory by which that Law is now "explained" may be modified or abandoned some day. Perhaps, referring to the italicized sentence at the end of the preceding paragraph, one can say that the experimental findings or observations expressed by factual statements are permanent—even though their interpretational aspects are subject to change and regarded as transient.

6 · COMMUNAL PERCEPTION AND CONCEPTUALIZATION

It should also be realized more than it is that the most important *scientific* facts are achieved typically through group or communal rather than individual "perception" and conceptualization. This has been shown with great cogency by the late Ludwig Fleck, microbiologist, in a remarkable, though apparently little known book entitled (by my translation from the German) *Origin and Development of a Scientific Fact: Introduction to the Doctrine of the Thoughtstyle and Thoughtcollective.*[6] The particular fact whose evolution he has analyzed in detail is the discovery that the Wassermann reaction is specific in the diagnosis of syphilis. He shows how this unit of knowledge (fact) came into being slowly and as the result of the labors of many scientists, and that it was therefore a truly communal achievement. He suggests, however, that it came about not so much because there was deliberate collaboration, or even a convergence of findings by independent workers, as because the thinking of many individuals was determined to a great extent by the common style of thought (*Denkstil*) and the compelling thought pressure (*Denkzwang*) of the scientific community, which he very appropriately and ingeniously thinks of as a thoughtcollective (*Denkkollektiv*), or fellowship of thought (*Denkgemeinschaft*) and mood (*Stimmungskameradschaft*). He urges that this fact is typical of the facts of science, as distinguished from the more obvious ones of everyday life, in regard to both their nature and evolution. He criticizes with keen insight, and refreshing humor, the traditional accounts of how such facts are won. To quote him in somewhat free translation, he says: "There exists a widely propagated myth about observation and experiment. The understanding subject (as distinguished from the object to be understood) is portrayed as a sort of conqueror who like Julius Caesar wins his battles according to the methodological formula: *veni, vidi, vici.* According to this view, if one wishes to know something, one simply makes an observation or an experiment—and behold, one knows it. Even accomplished investigators who have won many a battle believe this naive fairy tale, when they consider their work in retrospect." He then cites much evidence to show that such naive views of science are no longer tenable. And this is supported by an increasing number of anecdotal, biographical, historical and sociological studies of science as well as by psychological studies of perception and of other aspects of the winning of knowledge.

Epistemology must then, Fleck suggests, take into account more than simply the subject and object, namely the community. The concepts, theories and interpretations with which all observation is laden are in large part gifts of the community. Even the basic ability to "see" or observe scientifically is determined or conditioned communally. It is learned from more experienced "seers" or observers. Consider how difficult it is to see intelligibly with a high powered microscope, or by means of X-ray photographs. Considerable scientific sophistication is required. Nowhere is this more evident than in a new, hitherto unentered or undeveloped field in which there are as yet no other "seers" to learn from. One reason why progress there is difficult and slow is that one has no precedents or guide lines. One has actually to learn to "see," to observe, to inquire meaningfully by oneself. To ask fruitful questions at any time, i.e., questions that anticipate or foreshadow meaningful answers, requires that appropriate structures of meaning and of language be available for communication—and these develop only communally. In new fields these do not yet exist. Therefore, Fleck suggests, the epistemological model, if it is to be adequate for explaining the generation of knowledge, must be not merely the traditional duality of subject-object, but the trinity of subject-object-community. Moreover, in this connection both subject and community must be understood in genuinely human, personal terms, including the ever present communal directive pressures and compulsions, intellectual competition, emotional stresses, conviviality, passion and prejudices, as well as the more directly pertinent factors of common knowledge, modes of thought, conceptual structures, available intellectual tools and techniques.* It is complicated business.

7 · ABOUT TRUTH-CLAIMS

This then brings us to the climactic question of what truth-claims science makes. Here we encounter the difficulty that the term *truth* is not a scientific one; that is to say, it does not belong to the technical vocabulary of science. Nor is there, so far as I am aware, a scientific, as distinguished from a philosophic, doctrine of *truth*. Most scientists, when asked what it means, either in general or specifically in science, seem to feel somewhat embarrassed. They don't know quite what to say. If pressed, they are likely to reply that this is outside the area of their competence, that it is a question for philosophy rather than science, that the question was never raised as part of their graduate training, that they have never lectured or written on the subject. The fact is that one can work through a large number of scientific treatises without ever encountering the term. One does not need to consider explicitly the subject of "truth" in the research laboratory; indeed one can work with colleagues for years without ever hearing the word—except possibly when a group has taken time out from its scientific work, and is philosophizing informally during, say, a coffee break.

To get on with their business, scientists do not need to worry about such questions. Science is the kind of existential enterprise, and scientists are the kind of people that ask: Can I, or we, count on this being true? rather than: What is truth? These are two very different questions. And yet all scientists would claim, I think, that the twenty-two statements listed in Table I are *true,* permanently and certainly. And this claim they would make † using the term *true* in a common-sense meaning. What they would mean is that there "really is" such stuff as oxygen and hydrogen. They are not fictitious products of the imagination—such as the well known pink elephants or leprechauns. You can buy them, oxygen and

---

* This has been explored at length and with keen insight by Polanyi. See earlier reference.

† Consciously or unconsciously—though I believe mostly unconsciously.

hydrogen, in hefty tanks. If you don't handle them with due care and respect you may be blown up. Likewise sound echoes are not hallucinations. You really hear them. And other people can hear them. Yes, to be sure, one can be fooled by them. But when one is sober one can easily enough avoid being fooled, especially if other sober and more or less intelligent people are present, with whom one can compare notes and who are able and willing to support, criticize and check one's hearing and concluding. In this sense the expression "to be true" means "eternally and unchangeably." None of this business of saying, This is true of nature now, but later on it may not be! No, if it is not *always true* one should not say *true*. Moreover, it means certainty, not probability. Another implication of "true" is "real" in its common-sense meaning. It refers to something "out there," that impresses itself upon us compellingly as given—*us* meaning in this case members of the scientific community who have learned to see and hear things together.

The mission of science is to unveil, study, interpret and transform a real, concrete nature—not an imagined one. It does this, of course, by analyzing and interpreting data of experience. It has therefore developed critical attitudes toward, and ways of treating, such data, in order to assure the identification of what is "true," "real," and "certain" about nature—in the common-sense meaning of these terms. Without saying at this time what are the ways the science community uses for thus assuring itself, I submit that such eternal-truth-claims as it makes apply to its empirical findings (circle *a* and Table I), but not to its theoretical constructions (circle *b* and Table II); to the "factual" stream of its ideas, not to the interpretive one in the history of optics. It would claim, I believe, that the laws of reflection and of refraction, or the insight schematized by the Mendeleev Periodic table, are *true* to nature, but would not claim this for any theory of, say, light or the internal structure of atoms.

Unfortunately,* however, it must be admitted that scientists are not at all agreed on what should be said positively about theories with regard to truth-claims. There are those who say that a theory may become more and more true as it is modified, or

* Or perhaps fortunately for the long run.

possibly less and less true if it is not modified to take new phenomena into account. There are others who speak of a theory as true if it is self-consistent, much as they would apparently speak of a geometric theorem as true if it follows logically from a set of postulates. Clearly, there is here a question of semantics. To use the word *true* in such ways may be quite legitimate, but it should be recognized that to do so amounts to talking about different aspects of theory, to which different meanings of *true* may or do apply. I suspect that the very large majority of physicists would agree that it is appropriate to think of the statements of Table I as true and representing reality.

From this point of view, however, the statements of Table II, regarded as theoretical, interpretive constructs of the minds— which is what they were when they were in vogue—should be considered as neither true nor false. As Poincaré said long ago, a theory is like a tool of thought or a language, and it makes no sense to speak of German or French as true or false. Rather one can say only that for a particular purpose the one may be more or less useful than the other. So it is with a theory. If it no longer functions properly in relating facts symbolically, or in predicting new phenomena; if it does not enable us to "explain" or interpret as well as does another, it is discarded. Therefore, among increasing numbers of physicists a theory is regarded rather as more or less useful, or fruitful or fertile, than as true or false. The theories of optics to which we referred are categorically different from the laws of optics. And their nature and functions are such that we make no *truth*-claims for them, but rather validity- and fertility-claims.

It makes good sense then to say that the permanent, certain, true-real aspect of science resides in its empirical findings, while its flexibility and adaptability, its impermanence and changeability, reside in its theoretical components—remembering that no sharp line of demarcation can be drawn between these two components.

When an hypothesis or theory is confirmed it unfortunately tends in time to take on the status of fact and therefore truth. People forget that they are constructs. Sometimes they even come to seem self-evident. This is what happened in time to most of the constructs of Table II. Then when they came under attack and were in process of disconfirmation it seemed that truth was being denied, rather than simply that theoretical constructs were being abandoned. Certainly if the statements of Table II are regarded as factual statements then they must be regarded today as false. What I am suggesting is that such constructs should not be allowed to be confused with empirical findings and should *never* be given the status of factual assertions.

8 · PERMANENCE AND TRANSIENCE IN RELIGIOUS THOUGHT

Are there permanent and transient elements in religious thought also? Religious beliefs are related to our deepest concerns, and profoundly affect our relation to God and fellow men. Therefore it matters very much whether what is believed represents permanent and certain insight or not. Moreover, if religious thought—like scientific thought—has components that are actually temporary, such as *ways of thinking appropriate to particular times and cultures,* or *imaginative interpretations, theories and explanations* that play a role somewhat similar to that of scientific theory, then it is imperative that they be recognized for what they are. They should not be mistaken for, or given the status of, permanent truth. In all other areas of thought there is the fixed and inflexible, as well as the yielding and elastic; the permanent that is determined by the intractable givens of objective reality, and the impermanent represented by the theoretical explanations and interpretations that are determined in part by its own growing insights and in part by the thought patterns prevailing, and changing, in the surrounding culture. Is this the case also with religious thought?

Are there then any beliefs or insights that succeeding generations of Christians have accepted as permanent and certain? Yes, many. Table III presents a few of them. Those of part A are general ones, some of which are shared by other religions also. Those of B represent more especially beliefs pertaining to revelatory events in the Judaeo-Christian tradition, out of which came some of those of part A. Without doubt the items of both A and B are widely regarded as permanent and certain insights.

TABLE III

Items of Religious Insight Regarded
As Permanent And Certain

A. General and Perennial Insights

    1. God has created and now upholds the world.
    2. He has created man in His own image.
    3. God is good.
    4. God is love.
    5. God is just.
    6. God is merciful.
    7. God came among men in Jesus Christ to save them from sin.
    8. God forgives.
    9. God makes known His will.
    10. God reveals His love for all men.
    11. God demands that men love and serve one another.
    12. God calls upon men to resist evil.
    13. God bestows upon men His Holy Spirit.
    14. God provides the necessities and blessings of life.
    15. God has conquered, removed the sting of, death.
    16. God bestows on men eternal life.

B. Specific Revelatory Events

    17. God "called" Abraham and covenanted with him.
    18. In the Exodus experience God delivered "His people" from bondage in a "miraculous" way.
    19. At Mount Sinai God gave "His people" "the law."
    20. Through the prophets God called men to social justice.

By contrast, in Table IV we find beliefs that were at various times regarded as integral to Christian belief, but have since then been abandoned by all but the most conservative segments of the Christian Church. When they were first called in question there was widespread opposition because it was felt that the very foundations of Christian thought and belief were being undermined. Admittedly this list is a hodgepodge of ideas chosen more or less at random. Some would say—by way of hindsight—that they should not have been regarded as *religious* beliefs in the first place. Nevertheless they illustrate the thesis that religious ideas once current may later be discarded. I feel certain that virtually all theologians would consider them unacceptable today.

Now the question arises, as it did with respect to scientific

TABLE IV

Abandoned "Religious" Ideas

1. The Bible is historically inerrant.
2. The Bible is scientifically inerrant.
3. The worship of God requires sacrifices of flesh and blood.
4. It is God's will that the enemies of "God's people" be annihilated in time of war.
5. There is a real place in space called hell. *or heaven*
6. Sinners who do not make their peace with God are after death consigned to "eternal hell fire."
7. There is a real place in space called heaven where God sits on a throne.
8. There are personal beings called angels with spiritual bodies and with the power to intervene in nature and men's lives.
9. There are, similarly, personal evil beings called demons.
10. God created the world several thousand years ago.
11. After the world had been created for some time God destroyed virtually all life on it by a deluge that covered the whole planet, and only those human beings and animals were saved that were in a ship called Noah's Ark.

thought, whether it is possible to differentiate between the permanent and the expendable in principle, and whether this would enable us to make sense out of this dual, and apparently paradoxical, nature of Christian thought. Again the answer is, I think, both simple and profound. There is such a principle and it is the same one that applies in scientific thought. As we have seen earlier, religious thought has operated at two levels, or to put it in another way, in two different realms: first, that of the tangible, existential world (*Lebenswelt*) where men experience good and evil, love and hate, physical and spiritual hunger, peace and war, justice and injustice, the holy and the diabolical, redemption and forgiveness (circle *a*); and second, that of a more abstract and imaginatively constructed world inhabited by interpretations and explanations, by symbolic and mythical thought structures, personalities and entities, such as demons and angels, hells and heavens, and so on (circle *b*). While it should again be emphasized that the kinds of thinking representative of these two levels are not altogether independent or sharply separable, they are significantly different. The one is in the main experiential or empirical, and the other interpretive or explanatory.

Subsequent analysis will show, I think, that the kind of belief represented in Table III expresses what the community claims to have experienced (circle *a*), and represents insights that have come out of the experiential faith relationships between man and God. They are not to be thought of as abstract intellectual propositions deriving from involved systematic reasoning, but as insights resulting more directly from the community's having experienced mighty deeds of God.

The beliefs listed in Table IV are, however, quite different in nature. They represent the kind of thinking that characterizes the other level on which religious thought operates, namely the ways of interpretation and explanation that employ models and symbols that necessarily change in time as a culture's general thought patterns, needs of communication, cosmological images, and metaphysical categories change from generation to generation. This is where we meet theology, and here we encounter the transient elements of religious insight.

As we shall see in Chapter IX, there have been two streams in the history of religion just as there have been in science, the one empirical and experiential, the other theoretical. The former represents, as in science, the gradual accumulation of permanent insight, and the other the succession of transient explanatory conceptual schemes. To clarify this, it will be necessary for us to consider another subject which for many persons is a source of great perplexity and therefore a roadblock to understanding, namely the subject of creeds. This we do next.

CHAPTER VII

Digression on Creeds

In Religion and *Science?*

1 · WHAT ARE RELIGIOUS CREEDS?

Many people, if asked whether there are any permanent beliefs in religion, would reply, "Yes, altogether too many, and too permanently! Look at the creeds." Therefore it will be advisable, before continuing with our analysis along the lines of the last chapter, to take time out to look carefully at creeds—and related matters—both to see whether they deserve the harsh treatment they so often receive, and to lay a foundation for a more complete study of the permanence and transience of religious thought.

What is a religious creed? I suggest the following as a first approximation to a definition: It is a series of statements or affirmations that express, first, the fundamental faith relationship (*fiducia*) between a religious community and its God; and second, the basic beliefs (*fides*) that have come out of and in time developed in that relationship as it has been lived out in the historic world.

Most Jews would assert, I am told, that Judaism has no creeds. And yet the Jewish community has gained insights as the result of its long historical experience. One of these that came into being long before there were any Christians, and is still recited faithfully by Jews throughout the world today, is the following: "Hear, O Israel, the Lord our God, the Lord is One." What a profound insight! And it came in essence not from metaphysical or theological reflection but from living, and from history. I hope it will not do violence to Jewish sensibilities if I call this mighty affirmation a creed.

Consider also the so-called *Apostles' Creed* that is recited

THE APOSTLES' CREED

I believe in God the Father Almighty; Maker of heaven and earth.

And in Jesus Christ His only begotten Son our Lord; who was conceived by the Holy Ghost, born of the Virgin Mary; suffered under Pontius Pilate, was crucified, dead, and buried; he descended into hell; he rose from the dead; he ascended into heaven; and sitteth at the right hand of God the Father Almighty; from thence he shall come to judge the quick and the dead.

I believe in the Holy Ghost; the holy catholic Church; the communion of saints; the forgiveness of sins; the resurrection of the body; and the life everlasting. Amen.

liturgically by many Christian congregations at frequent intervals. This also is an ancient profession of faith. Some of its phrases date back to the second century A.D. and were current among the early Christians. It required several centuries to sift such phrases, to reject some, accept others, and finally to weld them into a coherent statement that was acceptable to the Church. It was acceptable because it truthfully symbolized what the Church knew it had experienced and what it hoped for. Millions of Christians since then have recited this creed with glad hearts, and many have given up their lives rather than deny the faith it expresses. Fundamentally this creed constitutes simply a confessional witness to realities that have been lived—and continue to be lived—by the Christian community, not the culmination of elaborate reasoning and philosophizing. Christians of some denominations deny that they have a creed. There can be no doubt, however, that those basic beliefs on which virtually all Christians *are agreed* are those expressed by this creed.

This last assertion may seem hard to believe, for there have been many sharp, acrimonious differences among Christians over their creeds and much blood has been shed because of them. Therefore some clarification is called for. In the attempt to provide it we need to consider several characteristics of creeds. The first one is that characteristically they are expressed in symbolic language that is not intended to be taken literalistically.

2 · THE LANGUAGE AND INTENT OF CREEDS

In both science and religion insights are in part ineffable. What is experienced and known always comprehends more than can be expressed in language. But the ineffability of religious insight is of quite another order than that of science; and the problem of communication, as well as that of initial understanding and conceptualization, is much more difficult. Human experience has shown therefore that the insights of religion require for adequate utterance the warm, "expressive depth language of symbolism," of legend, parable, metaphor, saga and myth, much more than the "discursive, precisely denotative steno-language" [1] and mathematical shorthand that characterizes, say, symbolic logic and theoretical physics. Only the former can convey or evoke enough of the richness, depth and intensity of the emotions, anxieties and personal involvement that characterize religion—and the horror of evil and sin, the beauty of holiness, and *agape,* the love that "passeth understanding." On the other hand, only expository, prosaic steno-language, together with the symbols of mathematics, are at all adequate for the needs of scientific discourse, where one must stress the precise and quantitative, the objective and impersonal. Moreover, while the latter is a necessary part of religious language, the former is not at all a part of scientific language.

Consider the biblical question, Who is *my* neighbor? and the problem of adequately stating and answering it linguistically. In the first place, what kind of a question is it, scientific or religious? It may be that when it was put to Jesus it was for disputatious reasons, and it was a matter of purely academic interest. In that case perhaps it should have been put simply as, What does the term *neighbor* mean? or Who is *a* neighbor? Clearly such questions call for careful definition, sociological data, statistics and curves. On the other hand, as: Who is *my* neighbor? it is an existential question calling for much more than a sociological answer. And how very much more the touching story of the compassionate Samaritan does tell! Indeed after it was told nothing more remained to be said. There was a compelling reason why Jesus spoke so often in the warm, expressive language of the parable, rather than in the kind of discursive and analytic language that is used in ethics or sociology. He had infinitely more to say.

Consider also the first pages of the Bible. How far one would miss the mark if one were to interpret them as historical and scientific exposition! Surely their intent is to affirm a glowing faith in the Creator-God—as is the intent of the entire Bible. Certainly their language is poetic and symbolic; not denotatively scientific. And the reason for this is that they have so much more to say than could a scientific treatise. To affirm or confess a faith is vastly different from asserting that something is true scientifically or historically, though these may be related in important ways. But to express a faith adequately is impossible without the language of faith.

Returning now to creeds, there are admittedly many people who are horrified by the Apostles' Creed because they feel that what it affirms is utter nonsense, or at least utterly meaningless, and that to believe it would be "unscientific" and unreasonable. They feel that it is a jumble of ancient ideas that became fossilized and outmoded long ago and are now untenable. They ask: How can anyone in this scientific age believe that there exists a God who has begotten a son, and a ghost-spirit who impregnates a virgin? And who with the conceptions of modern cosmology can believe that any man can ascend, go *up* in defiance of gravity, to a place called heaven; and who can suppose that in this alleged heaven there is a special place designated as being at the right hand of God? Such phrases and conceptions, they would say, no longer convey any meaning—unless, indeed, they do convey nonsense meanings.

But I would plead that this completely misses the point of the creed, namely that what it really confesses and affirms is a faith in God and a belief in his fatherliness. Moreover, this kind of objection rests upon the mistake of reading obviously symbolic language as if it were literal prose. This is then not at all a clash of science with basic religious beliefs and teachings,* but a clash with mis-

---

* I refer here to the undistorted teachings embodied in the Good News— not to later misplaced, literalistic emphases and interpretations, such as those of fundamentalism.

conceptions of the fundamental intent of those teachings, and it results at least in part from mistaking religious, symbolic language for literal, reportorial language.

Let us analyze its intent in some detail. Clearly it is first of all a confession of fiducial faith in God. "I *believe in God* the Father . . . , and *in* Jesus Christ . . . , *in* the Holy Ghost (Spirit), . . . *in* the holy catholic Church. . . ." But, of course, it is also an affirmation of fideistic belief. The truths believed or beliefs professed are not, however, of either a philosophic or scientific nature. They are not presented in the form of propositions about the reality or existence of objects or beings. Thus there is in this creed no explicit affirmation that God exists, or that Christ does, or that the Holy Spirit is objectively real. There is indeed nothing there that seems to be capable of adequate expression in philosophical or scientific language. Rather they are of the kind expressible only by the warm, expressive language of symbolism.

"I believe in God *the Father.*" How wonderfully expressive is this obviously symbolic language! God, as Father, provider, one who cares! We are reminded of the prodigal son, who, when he had spent everything he had, when he was down and out, alone without friends, and despised, said "I will return to my father." He will still care. We are reminded also of the father, who, when he saw his son at a distance, recognized him at once, promptly gave orders to insure his proper reception, and then himself went to meet him on the road and welcome him home. What is affirmed and *believed* is that God is like that! First we have the confession of faith, a *believing in* God, and then an affirmation of the *belief that* this God is the Father kind of God. Incidentally, how far one would miss the mark if one were to become prosaic about this beautiful symbolism—if one were to ask whether this means that God is married, or if one were to ask the question that comes up so often, whether this allegedly anthropomorphic God has arms and legs, or a grandfatherly beard. This is not the sort of thing that is referred to or affirmed here.

Next, "I believe in God the Father and in Jesus Christ, His only *begotten* Son . . . . *conceived* by the Holy Ghost (Spirit). . . ." Should we now become prosaic about "begotten" and "conceived"? No! In the realm of human life, how rich with meaning are the words "begotten" and "conceived" for a man and a woman who have the great good fortune of being parents together. Yes, they do refer to biology and sex. But do they not also signify much more? Do they not mean an indescribable giving and receiving without reservations, a complete union of bodies *and* spirits, a way of self-fulfillment achievable only through love that creatively brings into being a new life, and another love? I say that here, in the very heart of this creed that expresses the Christian faith, the words "Father," "begotten Son," "conceived of the Holy Ghost," symbolize the belief that is the central message of the Bible, namely that the almighty creative force in the universe and in human life is love—the love that is God and comes from God. We certainly do not have here a metaphysical proposition on existence. But there *is* a truth claim here, as well as a profession of faith.

When we pass to the phrase "born of the virgin Mary" we encounter the same kind of affirmation and belief, namely that this particular birth was something special. Certainly with it the course of history changed. Through it powerful spiritual forces were released into the world—forces that many men and women since then have experienced as truly redemptive and liberating. For the early Christians it meant nothing less than that through this birth God had come among men—or to use theological language, God had become incarnate. *This* is the belief confessed. This is why no ordinary language would do in referring to it. The most powerfully suggestive idiom and thought pattern available at the time for speaking of so momentous a birth was "born of a virgin." Only *it* could make this birth seem at all credible and convey all the wealth of meaning intended. Again we have first a confession of faith in God, and then a truth-claim about the kind of God he is.

Whether Mary was or was not a virgin physically seems not too important in the light of the reality of the remarkable act of God that the expressive image of the virgin birth symbolizes. Let me acknowledge, however, that many Christians have interpreted the virgin birth of Jesus literally. Indeed, some denominations insist on it. The same is true of other phrases of the Apostle's Creed, such as "descended into hell," "ascended into heaven." It is altogether possible, even probable, that the early Christians too thought of them literally. Certainly their biology and cosmology would by no means have excluded the possibility of a virgin birth, a descent into the lower regions, and an ascent into the upper, or celestial, regions. Indeed for approximately the first fifteen centuries A.D. there were no compelling scientific or philosophic reasons for thinking any other way. Virtually everybody thought in such terms. What is important in this connection is, however, that even so, even though the early Christians doubtless did think of the virgin birth, the resurrection, the descent of Christ into hell and His ascension as credible *physical* events, they most surely regarded them as symbolic in their meaning and significance, pointing to God's fatherly redemptive love, symbolic of the revelatory, liberating experiences God had vouchsafed them in the coming of Jesus Christ.

The intent of this creedal language was then first to confess a faith and, second, to profess beliefs emerging from that faith. These beliefs are not those that strike the eye first if the creed is read literalistically. Rather they are the ones that become beautifully and convincingly clear when the poetic, symbolic and warmly expressive language in which the creed is written is allowed to speak to one's heart and mind. About these basic faith-beliefs it can be said also that they are shared by virtually all Christians, however much they may disagree about those that come out of literalistic reading.

It may be helpful to point out that this tendency to mistake symbolic language for literal language is not unique to religion. Teachers in the humanities say that one of their most serious difficulties is the tendency of students to read poetry like prose. As a teacher of physics I am painfully conscious of similar difficulties with respect to scientific symbols. I am not referring here to the so-called mathematical symbols, i.e., letters or numbers representing quantities, such as x and y and π, but to the symbolic words and concepts of science and to the symbolic structures we call theories. Consider, for instance, the theory symbolized by the term "Bohr atom." This theory makes use of images. It pictures an atom as a miniature solar system, with a massive nucleus at its "center," with electrons of small mass revolving around it in orbits. Light is emitted when an electron jumps from one orbit to another. Unfortunately, what most people seem never to learn * is that this picture, or model, is purely symbolic. It is not descriptive in the ordinary sense. It is not intended to tell how the atom actually looks. Its purpose is explanatory and predictive in the scientific sense. So far as we know, there are no such orbits in nature. They "exist" only in the symbolic scheme. And yet the tendency persists to think and talk of them as actually existing concretely, i.e., to interpret the symbolic scheme literally. As in the case of religious symbolism, this is to miss the whole point of theoretical physics, as it is conceived today. Moreover, it leads to serious misunderstanding and paradox within science itself, and, as I shall try to show later, causes clashes with religion—just as misplaced literalism † in religious thought makes for clashes with science.

3 · ARE CREEDS UNCHANGEABLE?

A charge brought frequently against the Church is that its attitude toward its creeds is one of inflexibility and unchanging rigidity. While science is always ready, so one hears, to change its beliefs when occasion demands, i.e., when better ones come along, religion is not. Once the creed of the Church, always the creed of the Church!

Again I plead for a different point of view, one that takes into account more of the facts of the case. And the important facts to be noted are, first, that the history of creedal development is a long and complex one, indicating that creeds have in general experienced many vicissitudes by modification, expansion or contraction, elimination and replacement, and, second, that the attitude of the Church toward them has been varied and changing.

Anyone seriously interested in the truth of the matter should at least look into, if not actually carefully study, a three-volume opus entitled *The Creeds of Christendom,* by the distinguished church historian Philip Schaff.[2] He is likely to be surprised to

---

* In many cases, no doubt, because of faulty teaching by scientists.

† Associated with this error of misplaced literalism in linguistic interpretation—and perhaps a variant of it—is that of supposing that a successful theory must be "true," true to, or of, nature, in a descriptive sense. This will be considered at length later.

THE NICENE CREED

I believe in one God the Father Almighty; Maker of heaven and earth, and of all things visible and invisible.

And in one Lord Jesus Christ, the only-begotten Son of God, begotten of the Father before all worlds, God of God, Light of Light, very God of very God, begotten, not made, being of one substance (essence) with the Father; by whom all things were made; who, for us men and for our salvation, came down from heaven, and was incarnate by the Holy Ghost of the Virgin Mary, and was made man; and was crucified also for us under Pontius Pilate; he suffered and was buried; and the third day he rose again, according to the Scriptures; and ascended into heaven, and sitteth on the right hand of the Father; and he shall come again, with glory, to judge both the quick and the dead; whose kingdom shall have no end.

And (I believe) in the Holy Ghost; the Lord and Giver of Life; who proceedeth from the Father (and the Son); who with the Father and the Son together is worshiped and glorified; who spake by the Prophets. And (I believe) in one Holy Catholic and Apostolic Church. I acknowledge one Baptism for the remission of sins; and I look for the resurrection of the dead, and the life of the world to come. Amen.

discover how very many official creedal formulations of various kinds there have been within Christendom. Each one of these represents an effort for various reasons to modify and improve upon earlier ones.

Sometimes what was needed was elaboration and clarification of the old in order to be able to cope with new situations, problems, or threatened dangers. An example of such a development is represented by the *Nicene Creed,* which was probably formulated in its present form in the fourth century A.D.

Now even only a cursory comparison of this with the earlier Apostles' Creed will reveal the kinship of the two. Clearly the later one is in a real sense an elaboration of, and an attempt to clarify, the earlier one. Whatever one may think of the content of this later creed, one must admit that it represents growth in thought, a willingness to face and to come to grips with new problems and new concepts, as well as to conserve old values and protect what was considered to be established truth from the inroads of error. There is no stand-pat-ism or rigid inflexibility in evidence here. Many of the additions or modifications that appear in this creed constituted at the time daring intellectual innovations, some of them intrusions from the Hellenic world. They evidence willingness to take philosophy and metaphysics into account, and to make the Gospel meaningful in terms of contemporary thought patterns.

When one reads early Church history, say that leading up to the Nicean Council of the Church, one encounters much talk about various heresies, and many theological terms that seem strange and forbidding, such as Chiliasm, Manicheism, Monarchianism, Patripassianism, Sabellianism, Arianism and many others, and one may develop a distaste for what may seem to be needless and meaningless hairsplitting. One may even get the impression that this was a time when the Church engaged primarily in suppressing new ideas, and in standing pat. But actually the situation was quite otherwise. It was a time of intellectual ferment in the Church, a time when new ideas were sifted and weighed against the old and tried—and when many new ideas were finally rejected and many others were accepted. And the new Nicene Creed was one outcome of it.

True, in terms of our present-day insights and ideas the development then was marred by heresy trials and excommunications of a kind we would find abhorrent. There was also much ecclesiastical-political maneuvering that we would deplore. But the fact is—and this is the point I want to make here—that there was momentous progress in thought; there was flexibility and adaptability, rather than stubborn, obscurantist rigidity. Nor did this display of flux and change, of assimilation and adaptation, cease with the development of the Nicene and other Creeds of the time.[3]

Sometimes the creedal picture has changed by other processes, e.g., as the result of revolution, or reformation, that eventuated in secession or schism, when a new church body came into being. In such cases the new communions felt the need of reformulated creeds that would give more adequate recognition to the distinctive insights that had been at issue. Thus there came about the many catechisms and confessions of the regional or national churches that emerged from the Protestant reformation, and still later the creedal statements of various denominations. However much we may decry or deplore the religious rivalries that resulted, and the divisive influences stemming from these multitudinous creeds and doctrinal formulations, from the point of view of long range history, the over-all picture they present is not one of static, rigid creedal unchangeability. While, to be sure, at any given stage of history some people vigorously opposed creedal change, others have pushed forward, insisting on new perspectives, interpretations, or formulations.

During recent decades there has been a tendency toward re-union of the shattered pieces of the Church. With this has come a recognition that many of the earlier creedal differentiations were nonessential and should no longer be insisted upon. A large part of the Church has come to realize that creeds all too easily become fossilized, and tend to devitalize, destroy and alienate. It has become apparent also that the language of many of the older creeds is so far removed from the language of everyday life as to make them largely meaningless. For many people they no longer convey the basic insights of the Christian message.

It is out of such recognitions and developments that the *Statement of Faith* (see p. 28) of the United Church of Christ was born. It may be said to represent at least four grave concerns of the committee that prepared it and of the church that accepted it: First, that it be a confession of the genuine, basic faith of the universal Christian Church; second, that it contain only what is fundamental and relevant; third, that it be couched in such language as to be truly meaningful in the twentieth century; fourth, that in its influence it be inclusive rather than exclusive, and cohesive rather than divisive. When it was adopted it was with the understanding, explicitly stated, that it was never to be used as a test of orthodoxy, or as prerequisite to church membership. It was felt that if individual Christians regarded the Statement as being truly expressive of their faith and beliefs, and truly descriptive of their own knowledge of and relationship to God, nothing more was needed.

Whether this Statement of Faith will actually meet these criteria in practice, in the life of the Church and the world, only time can tell. But its adoption on the basis of these ideals is of great significance as an indication of the attitude of much of the contemporary Church with respect to creeds.

4 · PERMANENT AND TRANSIENT ELEMENTS OF CREEDS

This brief sketch of creedal religious thought leaves no doubt that it has elements of permanence, beliefs that have persisted for a long time, that succeeding Christians have accepted and continue to accept as true, upon which they "bet their lives" and that they do not expect ever to have to relinquish. It is such everlasting beliefs that appear in Table III. And it is they that find expression in the Statement of Faith, as is evident from the language of the Statement of Faith which says, "to whose deeds we testify." The believer is here not an advocate spinning an argument or building a defense, but simply a witness presenting testimony of what he knows has happened in the past and continues to be experienced in the present.

This language is reminiscent of the opening verses of The First Letter of John: "That which was from the beginning, which we have heard, which we have seen with our eyes, which we have looked upon and touched with our hands . . . that which we have seen and heard we proclaim. . . ." When the early Christians went out into the world to preach the Gospel, they went forth to tell about and share that of which they were sure because of this remarkable, transforming experience, not because of philosophical or theoretical argument. And it is this *experientially-rooted belief* that has survived in time, and which the community regards as eternal. Permanence of insight is then associated with such belief. And, as in science, the community identifies the permanent with the certain and true—in the sense employed earlier for these terms.

On the other hand, there are also in creedal thought elements of transience. The first to be noted is the transience of imagery and linguistic expression. That it is important to distinguish between the basic message and content of religious thought and of creeds on the one hand, and the mode of expressing them on the other, becomes apparent from a comparative study of the language of the ancient Apostles' Creed and the contemporary Statement of Faith. In the latter there is no use of such language and imagery as "begotten son," "conceived of the Holy Ghost," "born of the virgin Mary," "descended into hell," "ascended into heaven," and "sitteth on the right hand of God." And yet this does not mean that the fundamental beliefs that were formerly expressed by such symbolic language are now being repudiated. Not at all! What is suggested is that at any particular time contemporary language patterns may be more effective for conveying the meaning of those beliefs to contemporary men and women. It suggests that fundamental *faith in* God and *belief that* God is love, need not be tied to a particular pattern of imagery and symbols.

It would be a mistake, however, to suppose that the transience of religious thought resides *only* in the changing modes of linguistic expression or symbolism, as these are responsive to cultural changes. No, it is also indigenous to communal thought itself as this grows and matures. At first faith and belief are simple and purely confessional; then they become more sophisticated as the need for explanation and apologetic defense arises. I-believe statements become relatively less experiential and more theoretical. Terminology becomes more philosophical. Experience itself becomes richer, and this in time enriches modes of expression and speculation. This is what happened in the historical evolution from the Apostles' to the Nicene Creed. Sometimes the enrichment comes by theological simplification, or the modification of formerly held doctrinal formulations or symbols. Something of this sort led up to the Statement of Faith. So we have continual interplay between communal experience and concepts, and therefore transience —just as we found such interplay in the history of optics.

5 · NO BARE FACTS IN RELIGION

In religion, as in science, no facts are bare. They are always mixtures of experienced data and constructed concepts, or even interpretations. In religion one does not "see" by simply opening one's eyes any more than in science. Always one sees with mental as well as physiological eyes, with the aid of one's ideas as well as with one's optic nerve.

As we have said, the Christian community would regard all of the assertions of Table III as factual, just as the science community regards those of Table I. But in both cases what is a fact is not merely a simple datum, but a hard-won unit of "knowledge," a complex of many data held together and made meaningful by a group of concepts or an interpretation.

Before proceeding, some parenthetical remarks are in order about the term *knowledge*. Many meanings of it abound in common usage. It is often said that there are different kinds of knowledge. In the sense usually intended this is certainly true. Thus to say "I know that this pencil is sharp," or "I know that my daughter loves her mother," or "I know that Shakespeare's plays are profound" is certainly to invest the term *know* with different meanings. Now many philosophers, especially those of science, seem to take the position that the term *knowledge* can be applied legitimately only to what is cognitively available through science, and that the arts and religion do not provide *knowledge*. Obviously this is, at least in part, a problem of semantics, but not one that can be solved in one swoop. My position is that it is preferable to use the term *knowledge* more broadly and that it makes sense to think of a continuous spectrum of knowledge (or knowledges) that includes the kinds involved in the three examples just cited, as well as many others. From this point of view one would then say that throughout the spectrum *one knows,* though the character of *what one knows* and *how one knows* changes from point to point within it. This will be explained further in Chapter X.

So then *a fact is a unit of knowledge,* as these terms are used here. And in neither science nor religion is a fact directly perceived. As pointed out earlier, the assertion that a given star is a hundred light years away is factual. But it is so only for those who interpret the data, such as the diffraction patterns and the values of angles measured, in terms of concepts, such as *star, light, speed of light, diffraction, parallax,* and of theories, such as those of physical geometry, celestial mechanics, the solar system. Likewise, the assertion that the Exodus was an event in history in which God delivered his people from bondage in a miraculous * manner is factual—but only for those who see sense in explaining a particular cluster of historical data in terms of such concepts as *event, God, God's people, deliver, miracle,* and of various theories, such as those of history, and of God's action in the world. In both cases one can say that the community regards these as facts because of what it remembers and *knows* has happened in its historical experience. *What is known* is different for science and religion, and in important respects *how it is known* is also. Yet both types of fact have two facets, the one experiential and the other interpretive. All facts are in part interpretations. None is a bare, raw datum.

Nowhere is this more evident than in connection with perspectives involving many data, as distinguished from more discrete perceptions, of, say, physical objects or phenomena involving only a few. As we have seen in Chapter VI, the general gas law is a complex, relational or perspective type of fact representing many data. One cannot point to any one dominant, directly-observed datum that itself essentially constitutes the fact, as one might in the case of a much more simple fact, such as that a particular confined body of gas has a specific pressure under certain specified circumstances. The same situation prevails in religious thought. Facts of generality or perspective carry a larger freight of interpretation or theory than do more specific ones. What happened, for instance, to Saul on the way to Damascus that transformed him into Paul, constitutes a relatively simple, direct and bare fact, as compared to what happened to the community of early Christians that led to the great perspective-insight that Jesus was the Messiah-Christ. Both are facts; neither is bare of interpretation, though one is much more so than the other.

Finally it should be remarked that as a class the facts of religion are without doubt less bare, and more laden with interpretation or theory, than are those of science. This is, however, only a matter of degree, not of fundamental difference, as far as this particular characteristic of all facts is concerned.

---

* The subject of miracles is treated in Chapter IX.

6 · CREED AND REVELATION

In Chapter II we discussed revelation as an important distinguishing feature of religion. We must now return to it briefly
since it has a bearing on creeds. In considering how insight is
come by, we said that in science one "takes hold" of what is investigated and intervenes in the natural course of events. To experiment means to impose controls, to manipulate nature, and,
so to speak, to wring information out of it. In religion this is impossible. There one is *grasped and given* insight—"by grace."
This does not mean that in religion one need not reason, or *do*
anything to gain insight. No, neither in science nor in religion is
full insight assured without both systematic disciplined reasoning,
and the unearned, unplanned-for burst of vision. And yet there
is this radical difference, that, in an important sense, in science
new understandings are, in the main, *achieved,* while in religion
the most fundamental ones are not.

It is to cover this difference conceptually, and to denote this
un-achievable, un-contrivable aspect of the gaining of religious
insight that the classical idea of "divine revelation" functions in
religious thought. Tillich has put it this way: "The word 'revelation'
('removing the veil') has been used traditionally to mean the manifestation of something hidden which cannot be approached
through ordinary ways of gaining knowledge." [4] There is in this
concept the idea of an active "revealer" that is quite absent from
the thought of science. According to the Judaeo-Christian tradition, insight comes because God deliberately discloses Himself.

Another concept that is pertinent here is the distinctively biblical
expression "Word of God," and allied to it the somewhat more
foreign Greek concept of "Logos"—to neither of which there is
an analogue in scientific thought. What these concepts convey is
that God has spoken and continues to speak, not, to be sure,
audibly or by some sort of inaudible dictation of specific words,
but through nature and history, through momentous events and
human experiences, through the Christ, through the inspired and
enlightened minds of men of faith and scholarship, through tradition and Scripture. And as He has thus spoken and as men have

heard and responded, there has been revelation; disclosure has taken place through "the Word of God" and there has been communication between God and man. Divine light has been shed abroad.[5] Far from adding to our knowledge of natural and historical phenomena, laws and principles, or answering scientific and historical questions, this Word of God both reveals and deepens for us the mystery of their being, and discloses the ground of their being and of faith in God.

In this connection it is of course necessary to speak of the Bible. Its existence, with all its consequences, constitutes an important difference between science and religion. Science has nothing that corresponds to the Bible, whereas for the Judaeo-Christian tradition its role is central and vital. It is difficult to conceive how there could have been such a tradition without the Bible. It is an integral part of the growing faith-and-belief structure and experience of "biblical" religion. About Christianity and the Church it can be said that they both produced and came out of the Bible. It may be said further that the Bible both contains a part of the Word of God, and is a part of the Word of God. However one may wish to look upon the Bible relative to God's Word, it is a fact that for Jews the Old Testament, and for Christians both Testaments, have been revelatory of God, His love and will. In this sense the Bible *contains* or transmits the revelatory Word of God—and yet may in an adapted sense even be said *to be* the Word of God.

Unfortunately, the nature of the Bible has been much misunderstood both within and without the Jewish and Christian communities; and in the relationships between religion and science it has been a source of controversy and estrangement. No doubt the basic difficulty has been that the Bible has been conceived of as a competitor of science as a source of scientific knowledge. This view has largely disappeared from Christian thought, for surely this was never its intent. The Bible records—though not historically as much as theologically—how God disclosed Himself as a living, acting God of goodness, mercy and justice. It does not purvey scientific knowledge.[6]

7 · CREEDAL PHENOMENA IN SCIENCE

Let us look at science to see if it has anything corresponding to religious creeds. We should do this not only because we are conducting a comparative study but because there is a possibility that we can understand religious creeds and creedal attitudes better if to some extent there seem to be scientific counterparts that seem to make sense—if there are any.

Does science have what may properly be called creeds? Well, if a creed is indeed a statement setting forth fundamental beliefs that have come to light in the thought of a community as it has lived out a faith relationship in the world, then surely the science community has creeds. Whitehead says it this way: "The dogmas of religion are the attempts to formulate in precise terms the truths disclosed in the religious experience of mankind. In exactly the same way the dogmas of physical science are the attempts to formulate in precise terms the truths disclosed in the sense-perception of mankind." [7]

Let us consider a few examples. Perhaps the most fundamental and significant one of all, certainly one hallowed by time and almost universal acceptance, is the so-called principle or law of cause and effect. It expresses the great insight that nature is orderly, and to a large extent predictable; that it can be trusted and does not cheat. Without it there could be no science as we now know it. Another is the principle of conservation of matter-energy. In its essentials it declares that nature is permanent, that its fundamental physical entity, unlike many of its forms, is not transient or subject to elimination or destruction. The dogma of Evolution (with an upper case E) * represents another such far reaching and fundamental insight. It is intimately related to the other two, since it also sees system, order, cause, and effect in the "natural history" of the world.

How have these great, all encompassing scientific insights and their creedal expressions come into being? In important respects like those of religion. They have emerged slowly and painfully

* As will appear later I distinguish between Evolution as dogma and myth and evolution as observed fact.

as the science community has struggled with difficult problems through the centuries. They represent revelatory disclosures that have come out of experience with nature, i.e., out of the observation of, and response to, and reflection upon it. Their emergence represents much more than immediate perception of isolated facts, but rather the intuitive recognition of general patterns that are not directly indicated by data. They are not conclusions drawn from particular experiments or sets of experiments. They express vision and insight about the totality of physical reality that transcends the knowledge gained in specific laboratory or field situations. What they stand for is not specific information, but over-all understanding.

A point to be emphasized is that the emergence of such overall insights and generalizations is not described accurately in terms of the logical tour-de-force, or the planned campaign of discovery. It is more like a gradual, or sometimes more abrupt, disclosure, a "coming to see," a revealing (unveiling) of what is not directly seen and seems mysterious. Initially it is the result mostly of imaginative extra- or trans-logical leaps of the mind; [8] and only later is it conceived and depicted as rationally necessary. Thus it seems to me to be both legitimate and meaningful to speak of revelatory experiences and events in the life of the community, and therefore of a phenomenon of "scientific revelation."

I hesitate to do this for two reasons. First, the word *revelation* is utterly absent from the vocabulary of science, and sounds so strange in the ears of scientists that virtually all of them recoil from it. Second, it is appropriating a word from another field, namely theology, and this often creates confusion. Nevertheless I do it to bring into bolder relief an aspect of science and of its similarity to religion that is overlooked too often. There need be no confusion, since by means of the adjective-prefix notice is served that the term "scientific revelation" is intended to convey a distinctive meaning, different from that of "divine revelation." While in this way an important distinction is emphasized, at the same time recognition is given to an important common factor.

What is common to them is the element of unplanned, uncontrived disclosure, a coming to see, an uncovering of what was not known, a vision and overarching perspective, a sudden bursting forth or a more gradual flowering of insight. What is not common to them is the kind of insight they lead to, and the source of the disclosure. In the one case man has himself attained insight about nature; in the other God has disclosed Himself to man.

To further emphasize this radical distinction I shall differentiate hereafter between *revealing* and *revelatory* on the one hand, and *revelational* on the other. The former will refer to both kinds of revelation, but the latter to divine revelation only. Thus events or developments in history leading to new scientific knowledge will be called revealing or revelatory, but not revelational, whereas those yielding faith in God will be designated revelational, as well as revealing or revelatory. In this way we emphasize that there is an added dimension or radical uniqueness in the revelational event that is not possessed by the merely revelatory one.

To add some concreteness to these rather abstract methodological and linguistic considerations, let us explore some of the interesting parallels here between religion and science—as evidenced by a legion of stories, legends and anecdotes. On the side of religion we have the phenomenon of revelatory experience coming to individuals, as illustrated by the remarkable stories of Job and Jonah, for whom truly revelatory experiences brought radically changed understandings—and in a real sense through no deliberate effort of their own. On the science side we have the same phenomenon and similar stories—witness the one about Sir Isaac Newton and the apple that fell somewhere on his anatomy and set off a momentous, revelatory chain reaction of thought concerning the universality of gravitation. And who could forget the delightful story of Archimedes, who had been thinking while taking a bath, and suddenly found the solution to a perplexing problem about a suspected "golden" crown, and leaped from there to the more general problem of objects in general, floating or submerged in any fluid— liquid or gas? The story goes that he became so excited about these overwhelming new ideas that he jumped out of the bath and ran down the street shouting, "Eureka, Eureka"—I have found it! I have found it! And to finish the story, we now require innocent beginners in physics to learn, recite, and accept the creed of Archimedes' Principle.

Then, too, there is the phenomenon of revelatory insight coming to the community as a whole, when essentially the same ideas or understandings occur to various of its members virtually independently in a relatively short time. The Protestant reformation is a case in point—when there came to churchmen all over Europe unorthodox revolutionary ideas about the relationship of man to God and to the Church, which eventuated in new doctrines, such as justification by faith, and the priesthood of each believer. Similarly, after many centuries of intellectual peace and quiet, revolutionary, revelatory ideas occurred to men of the science fraternity all over Europe within a relatively short time, that eventuated in the new astronomy and physics. In the one case there were Luther in Germany, Zwingli in Switzerland, Calvin in France (and later at Geneva), John Knox in Scotland, and many others rather close together in time, though far apart geographically; in the other Galileo in Italy, Kepler in Poland, Newton in England, and many others.

We who were graduate students in physics twenty-five or thirty years ago remember how remarkable seemed the bursting forth of the new quantum mechanics, when at about the same time the same basic ideas occurred, though in different forms, to De Broglie, Schroedinger, Heisenberg and Dirac, and still others, that turned physics into utterly unexpected directions. Similarly, about the same time there broke out the renaissance in theology [9] which, though it has not yet run its full course, has profoundly affected our thinking in religion. The names that come to mind symbolize insights which, though they certainly do not appear identical, together constitute revelation of great power for our time; among them are Temple, Barth, Brunner, Berdyaev, Aulen, Nygren, the Baillies, the Niebuhrs, Bultmann, Ferré, Tillich, and many others.

Surely these are instances of revelatory light breaking through to whole communities. Whence comes the authority of the creeds expressing such revelations? My answer is that it resides, in science as in religion, in their compelling truthfulness—which is not primarily metaphysical or theoretical, but empirical * truthfulness.

---

* "Empirical" is herein taken to be synonymous with experiential and observational. Experimentation is empirical, but to be empirical is not necessarily to be experimental. For my usage of the term "experience" see pp. 76–77 ff.

They are believed for the same reason they were brought forth in the first place. They have been experienced and are *known* to be true.

It would be a mistake of course to suppose that when the alleged apple fell upon Sir Isaac Newton the revelatory chain reaction of thought that followed came completely out of the blue, *de novo*. No, without doubt it came because the time was ripe for it. The concept of gravitation was by no means new. Much work and thought had been devoted to it previously, which, along with other historical circumstances, prepared the way for the coming of Newton and his tremendous vision. So it is in general as great revelations come in science—either to individuals or the community.

The same is true of divine revelation. There is in biblical thought the potent concept of "the fullness of time," according to which God acts in history to prepare man—and more particularly "His people"—for the decisive revelational event. In part this involves the shaping of earlier experience and understandings to make possible the reception of and response to the new disclosure when it comes. Thus the coming of Christ is thought of by Christians as the climax of a long process of preparation for that event through divine providence. As they see it, this is the main theme of the Old Testament. Similarly other revelational events are conceived as the culmination of God's preparatory action. They can truly *reveal* only in "the fullness of time" because their content and significance have in some sense been anticipated—even though not always correctly.

While scientists do not invoke the concept of divine providence or of divine preparation of the historical scene to account for the break-throughs of new scientific insights, their recognition and understanding of the actuality of previous preparation and conditioning, and of precursors to such break-throughs, is not altogether unlike those of the Judaeo-Christian tradition.

It should be noted that almost nothing has been said in this chapter about either scientific or religious theory. The reason for this is that in my view *fundamental* creedal thinking is not for the most part theological or theoretical in nature, but experiential. It belongs in essence to circle *a* (Fig. 2) rather than circle *b* (see

p. 69), to the factual rather than theoretical streams of history. Certainly this is true of such minimal creedal formulations as the Apostles' Creed and the Statement of Faith, that are primarily testimonial and confessional in nature. What they assert and witness to are certain remarkable revelatory happenings in the past and present history of the Christian community. They do not set forth theological, doctrinal constructions, but experiential happenings and discoveries. They exhibit the basic facts with which theology must work and which it endeavors to explain and interpret—not the constructs of theology.

In a sense then the role of theology in creedal thinking is subordinate in character. It helps in the construction of adequate and true testimonials. Its function in that connection is largely critical and analytical, to clarify, purify and verbalize. The concepts it peruses, rejects or accepts, are for the most part already represented in the vocabulary of the community at large, and are not the creations of postulational thinking. To be sure, as we have seen, later creeds tend to become more theoretically theological. But to the extent that creedal statements have taken on the character of miniature theological arguments or systems, rather than witnessing affirmations, to that extent they have departed from their fundamental purpose. That much of the Church feels this way about it today is evidenced by the tendency we have noted to return in the newer creedal formulations (e.g., the Statement of Faith) to the more primitive confessional affirmations of the early Church, and thus to focus attention upon the basic Christian creed, and to eliminate from it as much as possible the philosophical, metaphysical, theoretical constructions that do not belong there. This is not to discount theology, but only to say that in creedal thought it does not occupy the center of the stage.

The same is true of the relation of scientific theory to what I have called scientific creeds. In my view the latter represent insights that have emerged more directly out of revelatory scientific experience than out of creative postulational theorizing. Certainly this is the case for the creedal insights of cause-and-effect, conservation, and evolution. This will, I think, become clearer in subsequent chapters.

8 · DOGMATISM

At this juncture there arises the following objection. It is said that religion is typically dogmatic and intolerant about its creeds, whereas science is not; that the Church has foisted the creeds upon its members on authoritarian rather than rational grounds, that it has used force to assure their acceptance, and that at its behest men have been tortured and put to death for heresy. Before proceeding let us be quite frank about this. Religions have indeed been guilty of gross misuse of creeds, and of shameful acts against those who have rejected them. Certainly, as far as the Christian Church is concerned, this is a terrible blot on its record. Unfortunately, in more places than we like to admit, creeds still represent rigidity and obscurantism, divisiveness and exclusiveness, and constitute the justification for ostracism or persecution. No one is more keenly conscious and ashamed of this than many of those who are within the Church. But, having granted all this—and granted it without reservation—some other things need to be said.

The term "dogmatic" has desirable meanings also. It need not mean intolerance. Creeds and dogmas can be used properly, as well as improperly. They can unite, as well as divide, people. They can be reasonably elastic, not only unreasonably rigid. Moreover, creeds, in the best sense of the term, are both inevitable and necessary. We can't prevent their appearance, and we can't get along without them. And finally, some exclusiveness, such as is mapped out by credos, makes a great deal of sense; and so does a *judicious* amount of insistence that neophytes must learn and accept the basic creeds of a community.

To illustrate, while in science we don't ordinarily recite our creeds ritually, we do insist that they are important, and we do recite them on occasion. Certainly anyone wishing to be baptized into the community of *physics* is expected to learn, and subscribe to, Newton's Laws and the Principles of Conservation, and many others. Woe unto any freshman or sophomore who in a first indoctrination course in physics can't recite them at examination time! What would happen to anyone looking for a job as physicist, who said he did not believe in them? Needless to say, *he would not get the job*—and for good reason. What would happen if in some university a professor of chemistry were to post on the bulletin board of the chemistry department a series of propositions setting forth that the teachings of chemistry are to a large extent incorrect, that the periodic table of the chemical elements is meaningless, that the gas laws are nonsense, and that hereafter he would teach his own brand of chemistry—claiming it as his right to think for himself? The days of punishment by fire being in the distant past, he would not, of course, be burnt at the stake, but life would become rather uncomfortable for him. No one would deny him the right to think as he pleased, but everybody would agree that he should no longer be regarded as a professional chemist, or be paid good American dollars for teaching chemistry. And it is not altogether inconceivable that he might end up involuntarily becoming an inmate of another kind of institution.

In every realm of scholarship it is necessary to have creeds, summarizing I-believe statements, that set forth in general terms what has been found to be basic, that serve as the foundation of new advances, that express the common knowledge in a particular field, and the acceptance of which is regarded as the *sine qua non* of competence in that field. That, I submit, is the fundamental role of formal creeds in science and religion. It makes sense to say that creeds should not be misused, as they have been altogether too often in both religion and science. It does not make sense to say that there should not be any. It makes sense also to say that a person or a community should not be dogmatic or authoritarian—in the less worthy sense. It does not make sense to say that there should be no dogmas or communal authority. Moreover, it does not seem conducive to better mutual understanding between the communities of science and religion to keep referring to creeds as inherently bad, obscurantist and therefore perforce undesirable.

It seems undeniable that in the life of the science community there are creedal and revelatory phenomena that are in many ways equivalent in character and function to those of religion—indeed strikingly so. He who is aware of their existence there and truly understands their nature should not find it too difficult to appreciate what they are and mean in religion. As has been emphasized repeatedly, there are tremendous differences between science and religion. It is my contention, however, that in regard to creed and authority, revelation and faith, they are not as different as is commonly supposed, certainly not so different as to be inevitably irreconcilable in either basic attitudes or general method. On the contrary, with respect to these very matters that are so often cited as evidence of incompatibility, they are remarkably alike. And therein may lie one reason for believing that we *shall* be able to achieve a truly significant relation between them in our culture.

CHAPTER VIII

The Meanings of Concepts in Science

Also About "Verification"

1 · CONCERNING COGNITION

In pursuing further the question of the knowledge and truth-claims of scientific and religious thought, and of their certainty or uncertainty, let us address ourselves to an analysis of the basic meanings of certain types of concepts. Whether assertions or claims are to be declared acceptable or not, depends first of all, of course, on the meanings they are intended to convey.

It is commonly asserted that science deals with the directly and publicly knowable, whereas religion does not, since it is said to operate in the private rather than public domain. Science is therefore credited with dealing in publicly understood meanings and with having methods of verification whereby the truth of its claims can, at least in principle, be established or denied indubitably by anybody; whereas in religion, it is said, there is, and can be, no genuine verification. As might be expected, I shall deny that there is this kind of a difference. But, of course, prior to such a denial—or affirmation, for that matter—it must be clear just what is being denied, and this requires consideration of the question of meanings, and of ways by which they may be validated.

Clearly the questions raised here are in the realm of cognition. What is called for, however, is not answers that come from epistemological theory, but rather from the factual study of communal experience and practice in the acquisition and authentication of knowledge. While scientific and religious knowledge are radically different in content, it is not at all clear that they are so in the mode of their cognition. Indeed, as I see it, contrary to popular opinion, their "ways of knowing" are in essence alike. The theologian Daniel Day Williams puts it as follows: "All knowledge without exception is derived from a critical interpretation of what is given in human experience." [1] I suggest that a study of actual practice in the science and religion communities will clarify and confirm this with respect to their knowledge and insight, and this is precisely what might have been expected, if my portrait of their nature is accurate. For, what can be the significance of the threefold diagram, as far as cognition is concerned, but that the knowledge science *and* religion yield—in all of its dimensions, implications and consequences—results from experience (circle *a*) critically interpreted (circle *b*) and, may I add, transformatively applied in actual life (circle *c*)? * But before this can be shown successfully it is necessary to consider concepts and their meanings.

2 · TYPES OF CONCEPTS IN SCIENCE

There are, of course, various types of concepts in both science and religion. To illustrate, for science first, some are simply numbers, such as chemical valence, atomic weight and atomic number. Others, like speed, acceleration and work, are physical quantities, that may be defined, however, by means of mathematical relationships such as products and ratios. Thus speed is thought of as distance divided by time, acceleration as velocity divided by time, and momentum as velocity multiplied by mass. In speaking of these one must say something about *how much* or *how many* in terms of units. One class of concepts stands for various substances, or forms of matter, such as water, iron and nitrogen, while another denotes different conditions or states of matter, e.g., hot, soft, magnetic, electrified. Then there are two rather different types that signify respectively the large objects of the macroworld, such as rocks and clouds, plants and animals, and the tiny ones of the microworld, such as photons and the various subatomic particles. There are process concepts, e.g., freezing, coagulation, cell division, and evolution. A quite different kind of differentiation is that between scalars and vectors in physics. Vectors are spatially directional, as

* See diagram, p. 69.

are velocity, force and momentum, while scalars, such as temperature, plasticity and energy, are not.

Now when one reflects upon these and numerous other classifications of concepts, one is impressed by the implication that there is a surprisingly large variety of meaning and significance in science; further, that any one concept has in general more than one kind of meaning or connotation; and finally, that among those meanings that belong to a particular concept there are usually rather considerable and subtle differences in kind. To illustrate this last point, a concept may have one meaning that derives from its numerical character, another from its spatially directional nature, and still another from its being a peculiar kind of entity, a "something" that is, for instance, transferable from one object to another, and yet has no perceptible, independent existence of its own. Momentum is such a concept. It represents a mathematical relationship; its physical orientation in space is important; it does not exist by itself; it cannot be picked up or thrown like a stone; and yet in a collision of two bodies it may "pass" from one to the other. Energy is an even more peculiar entity. While it too is a mathematically relational quantity, it is, unlike momentum, a scalar and therefore does not have directional properties; but it does have another very different kind of property that is of vast importance, namely that it is transmutable into mass, and vice versa.

Now the question is: Does this kind of talk make sense? Does it *mean* anything? If so, what? Still more important for present purposes, if it does convey meaning, does it convey truth? In what sense? Are we talking about realities? Does energy really exist? In the same sense as a cloud exists, or a block of concrete? Consider the concept *electron*. Were electrons discovered or invented? Where do they exist? In our minds or in nature, or in both? What then does the term *electron* mean? Does it perhaps mean more than one thing?

Clearly such questions become important when we inquire into the nature of scientific knowledge and insight. Let us then ask what meanings any given scientific concept may have that relate especially to questions of existence, reality and truth. And first of all let us consider those concepts that refer to what may be called "unseen entities," such as space, time, matter, energy, light, electricity and magnetism, and the so-called discrete elementary "particles," such as molecules, electrons, neutrons and photons. In undertaking this I shall not proceed as philosophical analyst, but as physicist, using the language and thought patterns of physics, rather than philosophy. My purpose is to clarify "meanings in practice" that seem to pervade the thinking of physicists—even though many of them may not be explicitly conscious of it. The conclusions should be valid for the other sciences also.

3 · THREE-VALUED CONCEPTS

The thesis is that many concepts of science have at least three components of meaning that are respectively empirical, theoretical, and intuitive or presuppositional, in significance. One comes out of observational or experimental analysis (circle a), another from attempts to explain, correlate, predict and symbolize theoretically (circle b), and the third out of a "feeling in one's bones," a visceral, intuitive thinking, so to speak, an almost unconscious or even subconscious acceptance of things, or a taking them for granted.

The direction of my thinking may be indicated by reference to the well-known analysis by Professor F. S. C. Northrop of Yale, who has suggested that there are two kinds, or components, of concepts, namely concepts-by-intuition and concepts-by-postulation.[2] The former refers to what is "seen directly" or "immediately apprehended" in observation by what he calls "aesthetic intuition"; and the latter to what is cogitated theoretically, i.e., constructed or postulated. This profound analysis seems thoroughly sound and adequate for many—perhaps most—concepts of science. I suggest, however, that in scientific thought some important concepts have three rather than two components, especially those referring to "unseen entities" not directly observable, yet thought of as existing in nature, and as having "behavior" which may be investigated. Such concepts seem to have three significantly different components, or meanings, that I shall designate meaning-by-experience, meaning-by-postulation (in Northrop's sense), and meaning-by-presupposition or -by-intuition. After considering these three-valued concepts we shall turn briefly to the more common two-valued ones.

4 · THREE MEANINGS OF "LIGHT"

To illustrate this thesis, and to connect it with Chapter VI, we shall again consider the concept of light. In doing so attention is invited to Table V (pp. 144–145), which in columns A and C recapitulates what was said earlier about the two streams in the history of optics. At the left of the Table the quotation marks that enclose the term *light* symbolize an initially noncommittal attitude as to meanings. We start simply with the literal configuration of ink "light" (and corresponding sounds) and ask what it means to physicists.

Column A presents what we have learned about the historical growth of both common and scientific experience that has resulted in an accumulation of empirical knowledge of light that successive generations of physicists accept as permanent and factual, and do not expect seriously to modify or replace. If by scientific truth we mean permanently accepted knowledge that the science community considers beyond serious doubt, this column represents such truth. Again I am not appealing to any doctrine of truth, but simply describing or reporting—neither defending nor advocating.

Column C presents the succession of what may variously be called explanations, interpretations, hypotheses, conceptual structures and symbolic theories that are in perpetual flux. Here then we have not permanent truth, but passing ideas—judged in terms of usefulness, fertility, explanatory power, and predictability.

Column B is very different. It presents no historical development. It calls attention to the "intuitive" element of our knowledge of light, or of the process of gaining that knowledge. Whereas in A there are exhibited, so to speak, the products of conscious, deliberate observation and reasoned empirical analysis (experimentation), and in C the products of deliberate mental construction and postulation, in B we display the product of a more immediate awareness, perhaps what Northrop has called "aesthetic intuition," namely an unstructured belief or presupposition that may be characterized as primitive, subconscious, instinctive and unreasoned.

A

a. experiential meaning

b. concept-by-experience
   -by-empirical analysis

experience of lightness and darkness,
   seeing; also that experience extended
   instrumentally

TABLE V
Three Meanings
Represented
by the Symbol
"Light"

I. Common experience
   day and night, sun, moon, stars
   luminous and illuminated bodies
   seeing: at a distance
           with mirrors
           with lenses and prisms
   colored bodies
   warmth, radiation

II. Scientific experience
   reflection
   refraction
   dispersion
   diffraction
   polarization
   time lag, velocity
   "invisible light"
      ultraviolet
      infrared
   "electromagnetic light"
      radio, radar
   Ionizing radiation
      x-rays
      gamma rays

It is the idea, conceived in the dim past and inherited and accepted ever since without conscious rational justification, that there is an entity, influence or agent, a something that can separate from its source, traverse space, and makes things visible. Though presumably the eye is responsive to it, it is never "observed" directly, since one does not "see" light itself, but only the objects emitting, or illuminated by, it.

There are then at least *three meanings* represented by the symbol "light," and three components of the concept *light*. To say what one means by it, one must refer to all three. The first, "light A,"

B	**C**
a. intuited meaning	a. theoretical meaning
b. concept-by-intuition -by-presupposition	b. concept-by-postulation
intuitive, non-conceptual apprehension, or sensitivity to an entity, stuff, influence called light inherited-presuppositional	imaginative "explanations" or theoretical symbols of the experience of lightness postulations of the nature and behavior of the entity light

C (continued):

I. Common explanatory schemes
    something stored above
      firmament
    radiation from eye
    radiation from luminous
      bodies
    interaction of two
      radiations

II. Scientific theories
    symbolic structures
    corpuscular
    undulatory (wave)
      elastic solid (aether)
      electromagnetic (aether)
    neo-corpuscular (photons)
    wave-particle
    purely mathematico-
      symbolic, predictive
      models

refers to the many-sided human experience of lightness, as well as to the accumulation of scientific empirical knowledge. It is that component of the meaning of the concept *light* that comes out of reasoned, critical, empirical analysis of optical experience—out of scientific observation and experimentation. It illustrates what is meant by a concept-by-experience, or concept-by-empirical analysis.

The second, "light B," connotes the entity "light," or that "something" that enables us to see, to which our eyes and instruments respond, but which cannot itself be "seen." Since it is thus directly apprehended without the reasoned analysis involved in "light A," the existence of "light B" is taken for granted universally—intuitively. Even in beginning physics courses its existence is simply assumed, often without explicit mention or definition. This is an example of a concept-by-presupposition or -by-intuition. It may not be incorrect to remark also that it borders on, or points toward, the nonconceptual facet of knowledge.

"Light C" signifies the theoretical component of the physicist's concept of light, his attempt to explain imaginatively how the entity "light B" behaves in order to be experienced as "light A." More specifically it stands for the particular theoretical model (or models) of light that is (or are) current at a given stage of the history of optics. It is postulated, deliberately mentally constructed light, with properties defined by a system of equations, from which can be deduced functional relationships that will correspond hopefully to the empirically obtained equations, or laws, that define a concept-by-experience. Here, then, we have a concept-by-postulation.

It is important to realize that while no sharp boundary lines can be drawn separating these three kinds of concepts entirely, they do in general represent radically different scientific operations and conceptual worlds, worlds in which cognitive claims must be very different. There was a time, I think, when a physical theory was thought to be verifiable in the sense that it could be claimed as true, describing nature "pictorially," so to speak. It was regarded as a way of *inferring* what the unseen world is actually like, i.e., what it would look like, if it could be "seen." Today, however, there prevails a more renunciatory mood among many physicists, who no longer demand this of a theory. They do not expect a good theory of optics, for instance, to describe the entity light B pictorially in any sense, but only schematically and mathematically, by showing how various phenomena of light A may be correlated intellectually, and explained—by imagining that light B has the properties of light C. The world of C concepts is a realm of mental constructions, one's own or somebody else's creations. It is not the world of observable nature or of A concepts.

5 · VERIFICATION AND PROOF

There are several terms that are closely related and from the viewpoint of science seem to me to be very nearly synonymous, namely verification, confirmation, authentication, validation, proof and still others. They all stem from the concern of the science community that its findings be reliable and not illusory or false. It is important to recognize, however, that they have different meanings when applied to the three classes or components of concepts we are considering. That this must be so follows from the fact that they have different significance. Clearly a statement involving a concept-by-experience that makes a *truth* claim, and one involving a concept-by-postulation that makes a claim of *predictability* or intellectual fertility, should be regarded as "reliable" in different senses. And in the case of a concept-by-presupposition, when the claim made concerns *what is felt instinctively* or inherited culturally, "reliability" and "illusion" have still other meanings. The distinctions we must recognize are: reliably true, reliably useful or predictable, and reliably intuitive or presuppositional. Therefore the processes of authentication and confirmation must in these cases be different both in purpose and technique. This is precisely the situation in practice. Let us consider this in some detail, even though only briefly.*

To confirm an observational or experimental finding leading to a new concept-by-experience, e.g., a new scientific object, phenomenon or law, means, as I see it, essentially two things: first, making sure that the discoverer has not made serious mistakes, that he is not laboring under illusions or prejudices, and that other workers can obtain the same results; and second, making sure that the new finding does not contradict what is already known.

It has happened many times in the history of science that very competent scientists have announced discoveries that no one has ever been able to confirm. Within recent memory there have been at least two distinguished physicists who were awarded a coveted one-thousand-dollar prize of the American Association for Ad-

---

* This is, of course, a very large subject with many ramifications. The reader is therefore referred to the books on the philosophy of science.[8]

vancement of Science for outstanding papers announcing important findings, whose results have never been confirmed, and are therefore no longer accepted by the science community. In the case of one, he could not even duplicate his own results after the award was made. In neither case is there a shadow of doubt as to the man's integrity or competence. The point is that no matter how distinguished and competent a man may be, his results are not regarded as confirmed and authentic till other scientists have been able to report similar findings.

But even then this would not settle it if, for instance, the new findings did not fit in with what is already known. For instance, returning to the subject of optics, when the phenomenon of diffraction of light was first encountered it seemed very, very strange. For diffraction means that light bends around corners, whereas up to that time universal experience had been that light was propagated along straight lines only. This was definitely contradictory. Related to the phenomenon of diffraction there is another, called destructive interference. According to this phenomenon, light from one source may under certain circumstances be superposed upon light from another to produce darkness, rather than more lightness as one might expect. This seemed to make no sense either, and simple repetition of results by different people did not for quite some time seem enough to confirm such findings. What was needed was a showing that these apparently contradictory findings were after all in accord.

Now in this process of showing that contradiction is only apparent and that there is no "real" inconsistency, theory usually plays an important role, by showing how the apparently conflicting phenomena can be brought together under the umbrella of a single conceptual scheme, thus re-establishing logical harmony. In this way the phenomena of diffraction and interference were eventually shown to be quite consistent with what was known before, provided light was thought of as waves rather than particles. Later still, polarization was discovered, and this too seemed incongruous initially. Here the contradiction was resolved by postulating light waves to be transverse rather than longitudinal, as they had been theretofore. Thus the confirmation of new experimental findings calls for both experimental reliability and theoretical consistency. In some situations the former is more crucial and in others the latter, but both are important.

On the other hand, suppose that a physicist reports a new theoretical finding that yields a new conception-by-postulation; how is *it* "confirmed" as acceptable? [4] In this case the answer is more complex, and the resulting verdict in particular situations much less conclusive. In principle, however, the process is not too difficult to describe. Assuming that the hypothesis or theory in question meets criteria of internal excellence, such as simplicity, elegance and logical self-consistency, its validation externally is then achieved, first, by experimentally "checking" its specific theoretical explanatory and predictive implications, and, second, by showing that it can be fitted into the current theoretical scheme of things, or if not that it provides a new over-all scheme.* The latter simply expresses the demand that there shall not be permanent contradiction and incongruity. Either the new must somehow fit into the old with some consistency, or it must significantly modify or supersede the old in such a way as to create over-all consistency as much as possible.

Two things should be emphasized in this connection. First, such confirmation does not settle anything theoretically once and for all. When Maxwell developed his remarkable electromagnetic theory of light it soon became apparent that its explanatory and predictive power was very great. It successfully correlated and explained most of the then known facts of the behavior of light and electricity. Even more importantly, its predictive power was tremendous, as is illustrated by the work of Hertz which confirmed the prediction of the existence of electromagnetic waves with large wave length and thus opened up the whole field of what since then has become known as radio. Its success was so complete that many physicists came to feel that it provided the last word in the theoretical description of certain aspects of the world, that the physical world was known in its essentials, that thereafter research in physics would not lead to any new grand discoveries, but only to the further refinement of what was already known. And yet today that epoch-making theory no longer plays the central role it once

---

* Other reasons for accepting theories have operated also in the history of science. Some of these will be considered in Chapter X. See also Frank, *op. cit.*

did. Indeed for most purposes it has been superseded by newer conceptions. At the forefront of research it is of relatively little value today. Confirmation in the realm of theory and concepts-by-postulation is therefore only temporary, and what it validates is not truth, as we have characterized it, but explanatory and predictive power and usefulness.

Second, it needs to be emphasized explicitly that this validation of theory does not in any case constitute either experimental or deductively logical *proof* in the ordinary sense. The experimental "checking" of a theory simply must not be thought of as *proving* anything about it, except its *usefulness* for explanatory and predictive purposes. It was once customary to say that when one single fact is found to be contradictory to a theory the latter must be abandoned as false. But this is utterly misleading for two reasons. First, it is absolutely untrue. Theories are not abandoned in the face of lone contradictory facts. On the contrary, even the most successful theories fail to fit *all* the known facts. Second, a theory is not abandoned because it is false, but because it has become less *useful* than another.

Now what can be said about verification in the case of an assertion involving a postulate-by-presupposition? Suppose one were to say, "I believe that there is a something called light that is emitted by incandescent bodies, and can traverse space, that is responsible for vision and many other effects"; how could it be either validated or disproved? Or suppose one were to say, "there is light," or "light exists" (meaning light B); how could it be validated or disproved? I have come to feel that the only kind of validation that is possible, and in fact operates, in this case, is that of communal or intersubjective cross-validation and acceptance, i.e., evidence that others have also so apprehended intuitively and therefore make the same claim. By the same token the only kind of invalidation that seems possible with regard to an intuitive claim is communal rejection on the ground that other individuals and the community in general do not so intuit or feel justified in presupposing. If for instance a person were to claim that infra-red radiation is "visible" to him and that it has a color not known hitherto, but no one else could "check" this subjective claim, it would be regarded as not having been validated, indeed as invalidated.

The belief in the existence of light and our knowledge of it have then a threefold basis or aspect: first (meaning B), direct, intuitive, unreasoned apprehension and cultural acceptance; second (meaning A), reasoned analysis of the manifold optical experiences of light and deliberate experimentation with optical phenomena; and third (meaning C), the success of theoretical activity in the attempt to correlate, explain, apply and predict by means of imaginative mental constructions and hypotheses.

6 · THE THREEFOLD CONCEPT OF ELECTRICITY

There are, of course, other concepts of physics that are threefold in meaning. Electricity is one of them. It is fashionable to say that while we work with electricity, no one knows what it really is. But such a statement needs analysis, lest it give wrong impressions. I should say that we *do know* at least what electricity-by-empirical analysis (electricity A) *really is*. We can describe it in terms of many phenomena and experimentally established laws of physics. It is what happens when a wire is connected to, say, a dry cell, becomes hot and surrounded by a magnetic field. If we put an electrolytic cell into the circuit, certain chemical reactions take place in it. The meaning of this component of the concept of electricity is clear, and it represents what we actually *know*.

The theoretical component is also clear, though it represents ideas in flux. We *know* what electricity-by-postulation (electricity C) is, because we construct it mentally, though to "know" means something different in this case. We postulate electricity to consist of electrons that have certain postulated properties, such as those possessed by particles and waves. Thinking this way about electricity has enabled us to correlate many known facts and to uncover new ones.

When it comes to the third component of the concept of electricity (electricity B) our claim is different in kind. The question is, of course, a tantalizing one: just what is this subtle, elusive *something* that we presumably experiment with, that shows up in discrete quanta of charge, that exerts forces, and to which we ascribe postulated properties? What is its essential nature? This we do not know, and perhaps the question is not important to science.

The fact is, however, that physicists go on talking about and work-ing with electricity, assuming confidently that it does exist. Here then we encounter again a concept-by-presupposition, a belief or assumption that is inherited and accepted widely by succeeding generations of physicists—even though many epistemological ques-tions might be raised regarding it that have been largely disre-garded by the science community.

There is an interesting difference, however, between the *light B* and *electricity B* beliefs, namely in their history and presupposi-tional foundations. The former is ancient, and the latter modern. Not until about the seventeenth century A.D. did the science of electricity come into being. Until then there was nothing in the common and scientific experience of mankind that called for a con-cept of electricity. Lightning was simply a phenomenon of the weather. It had been known for a long time that amber when rubbed attracted light bodies, and that some eels now known to be electric had a disagreeable sting. But none of this meant "elec-tricity." Indeed the term was not used until the year 1646, in a book by Gilbert. The discovery of electricity constituted a break-through into the then utterly unknown. Until that time physics had consisted almost exclusively of the study of phenomena that could be seen, heard or tactually felt, and the existence of which therefore seemed intuitively self-evident. When therefore electricity first broke into the consciousness of man its existence seemed far from obvious, as that of light had been for millennia past. And yet in the relatively short intervening period since then it has come to seem quite as evi-dent—even without benefit of any sensual means for perceiving it directly. And so a part of our concept of electricity is now presup-positional.

In the history of the science of electricity there are also the two streams of growth of empirical knowledge, and of theoretical ideas. One could depict it also by means of a three-column table such as that for light. And column C would have an interesting succession of hypothetical models or mental constructs of electricity. It would list effluvia (enveloping atmospheres), subtle fluids, one and two-fluid theories, particle and wave concepts, and so on. And this col-umn would, as in the case of light, represent only what we can claim as useful, fertile, explanatory and predictive. Column A, on the other hand, would present what we regard empirically established, permanent and eternally true. And all earlier remarks about verification and validation would apply here also.

7 · SPACE

One more example of a threefold concept is called for, namely that of *space*. I choose this particular one because, while it is especially difficult for many people to differentiate between the three concept components in this case, it is also especially important that they be able to do so—if they would understand the nature of modern science.

It is well known, of course, that mankind's experience and knowledge of space has many facets, in which various disciplines have special interests. Late in the nineteenth century the celebrated mathematician Poincaré, in his analysis [5] of the content of the space concept, used such differentiating terms as geometrical space, representative space, visual space, tactile space, motor space. Other terms that have been used are natural space, physical space, stellar space, mathematical space, psychological space and so on.

Now, all these may be subsumed under three headings, attributing to the concepts of space and geometry the same three aspects that I have ascribed to those of light and optics. The Euclidian geometry taught in high school is a *postulated* structure. Its socalled axioms, from which its various theorems are derived, are not self-evident as is commonly supposed. They are conventional postulates chosen from an array of others that are also suitable from the viewpoint of pure mathematics. Euclid's geometry is then only one of many possible geometries, and what it presents is a particular mentally constructed space-by-postulation.

In measurement and experimentation, particularly those involving distances, however, the physicist deals fundamentally not with a postulated, but a physical, observed geometry, i.e., a geometry of measuring rods, so to speak, whose quantitative spatial relationships (theorems) are not derived by logical deduction, but by the measurements. If, for instance, it is desired to know what the sum of the angles of physically concrete triangles is in *this* geometry, one makes a series of measurements. One does this likewise to find out how the legs and hypothenuse of physical right triangles are related quantitatively. Moreover, one must always be prepared to find different relationships from those predicted by a geometry-by-postulation. This kind of a geometry or space concept is what I have been calling concept-by-experience or -by-empirical analysis.

There is also a geometry- or space-by-presupposition, i.e., one determined by intuition and instinct, as well as cultural inheritance, one that seems self-evident and almost non-conceptual. Unfortunately, however, until just a few decades ago these three concepts and kinds of geometry seemed indistinguishable. Indeed, except in the minds of a few pure mathematicians who knew better, there was simply one geometry, one space. The first, felt in one's bones, the second, postulated deliberately, and the third, dealt with in measurements, seemed one and the same. Not until Einstein shook us out of our intellectual prejudices and fossilized presuppositions did it become widely known within the science community that there are different geometries and space concepts. And most people outside of that community still have great difficulty understanding how there could possibly be any geometry other than the one that they learned in school and that has come to seem self-evident.[6]

In our universe, no doubt, the geometry felt in "one's bones," that of intuitive presupposition and of the ordinary unsophisticated space experience of the common man, will always be Euclidian. Until recently the geometry of the most sophisticated measurements was also Euclidian. But now there is considerable evidence, as the result of more extensive astronomical exploration of space and of the study of speeds approaching that of light, that the geometry-by-empirical analysis of precise physical measurement is not Euclidian. Meanwhile, the mathematicians have developed an array of postulated spaces that are not Euclidian. Which of these will turn out to be most useful for the description of the natural, physical geometry-by-measurement of the actual world remains to be seen.

Following our earlier analysis, I suggest now that it is with respect to a geometry-by-empirical analysis that we should make truth-claims, i.e., claims about what is objectively true of nature and given, and therefore is not merely a mental construction. As for a geometry-by-postulation, we should never claim for it more than that it is self-consistent, and that it may be more, or less, useful than another when applied to the actual world for explanatory and predictive purposes.

There seems to persist in the minds of many people the notion that truth and proof par excellence are to be found in a deductive system like Euclid's geometry. There, it is said, is where absolutely conclusive *proof* is possible and therefore where absolute truth can be found—if nowhere else. Clearly this is utterly erroneous. The fact is that a proof of a theorem in such a system simply consists in showing that it can be deduced by valid logical processes and that it follows from the postulates given initially. It tells us nothing directly about the natural world—unless it can be shown experimentally that the postulated system accurately portrays the natural world.

8 · OTHER CONCEPTS

Thus far I have identified the presuppositional component of a concept for the most part with a belief in an "unseen" entity or "reality" such as light, electricity and space. Matter, time, heat, magnetism and biological life are other such examples. A different kind of component-by-presupposition is contained in the concepts *cause, conservation* and *evolution*. There are still other types.

On the other hand many, perhaps even most, concepts of science do not have three components. The one that is missing usually in those cases is the instinctive, intuitive presuppositional element. As might be expected, the farther removed a concept is from the content of common experience, the more likely it is that this prescientific, subconscious, a-priori component will be absent. The concepts virtual work, entropy, electromagnetic mass, meson, tropism, protoplasm and artificial parthenogenesis seem to me to illustrate this. Probably all scientific concepts have at least two components, one by empirical analysis and the other by postulation.

9 · THE PRIVATE AND PUBLIC DOMAINS

In view of all this, what is to be said about the popular belief and assertion that science operates in the public, rather than pri-

vate, domain, in the sense that it deals with the directly and publicly knowable, and that it has developed methods of verification
whereby its truth-claims can, at least in principle, be established
or denied beyond question by *anybody?* The first thing to be said
is that it needs clarification, for as it stands it is largely meaningless. I should like to qualify it as follows. The world in which natural science operates is that part of the total world that the science
community has carved out for its particular attention and study,
that it has extracted or abstracted from the totality of reality and
existence, and for the exploration of which it has developed special techniques. Certainly this is true of physics.

Now this world has become rather far removed from the public domain of everyday life, from the world of experience and
thought of the common man, or even the un-common, highly informed and educated man who is not a scientist. To carry on research in the domain of problems that the modern scientist is concerned with requires a very high order of ability and training. It is
utterly unrealistic to assert that "anybody" or "everybody" could
verify for himself the findings of modern science. To verify the discovery of the wave nature of matter and the particle properties of
light, or of the Compton effect, or the findings of the Michelson-
Morley measurements, or the distance of a galaxy, is simply *not*
possible for everybody in any meaningful sense. And as one who
has taught physics for many years to students of all kinds I would
assert that it is not in practice possible for everybody to check for
himself even the much more simple findings of classical physics,
such as that the acceleration of falling bodies over short distances
is constant to a high degree of approximation, and that over large
distances it is not—to mention only one example. To say that it
would be "in principle" is to say no more, it seems to me, than that
no one is arbitrarily excluded from such a possibility. To be sure,
nobody is excluded, but relatively few are included. Actually scientists are today not, for the most part, working in the public domain, as the word "public" is usually understood, but in the much
smaller domain of the science community.

On the other hand, it certainly is true that science is not operating, or the least bit interested, in a private domain, such as that
of the experience and thought that is peculiar to a particular individual and cannot be communicated to and shared by others.

CHAPTER IX

The Meanings of Concepts in Religion

Verification and Validation

1 · THE THESIS

The thesis for this chapter is rather simple. It is that virtually everything said in the preceding one about concepts of science depicts also the situation in religious thought—recognizing, of course, that while this is true when stated in general terms, it is not true in regard to important particulars.

Again we find a variety of types of concepts and meanings, and for a given concept several meanings. Likewise we find the same two or three components of concepts, with the same implications as to truth-claims and verification, and the same two historical developments, one representing a gradual growth of factual, experienced insight and truth, the other a stream of interpretive ideas and modes of explanation. To illustrate these matters I again present a three-column table (Table VI, pp. 158–159), and the concept to be analyzed into components is that represented by the initially noncommittal symbol "God." While this is no doubt the most difficult concept in the entire realm of ideas, yet it is the most basic one in religion, as attested, for instance, by the significant fact that in the Statement of Faith every one of the articles of belief and faith relates directly to *Him*.

Here, by the way, is a truly significant difference between religious and scientific thought. In the one, certainly in the Judaeo-Christian tradition, there is a concept that completely dominates the whole structure of religious thought, namely that of "God." In the other there is no such all-powerful, overshadowing, significance-conferring concept. The reason for this is obvious, at

A

a. experiential meaning

b. concept-by-experience
         -by-analysis of historical
              experience

"God" as experienced personally and
   historically-communally

TABLE VI
Three Meanings
Represented
by the Symbol
"God"

1. Common experience of mankind:
   "God" experienced in
      worship, prayer, ritual
      the holy, numinous
      sacred place and time
      mystic vision
      grace and providence
      order and intelligibility of nature

2. Judaeo-Christian experience
   a. historical-communal

Event	God
Abraham's call	as covenanter
Exodus	as deliverer
Sinai	as law giver
Prophets	of social justice
Christ	as incarnate
Crucifixion	as conqueror of sin
Resurrection	as conqueror of death
Pentecost	as Holy Spirit

   b. personal
      agapé, self-sacrificing love
      love of neighbor
      grace, forgiveness, conversion
      miracle
      common work
      suffering

B	C
a. intuited meaning	a. theoretical, explanatory meaning
b. concept-by-intuition -by-presupposition	b. concept-by-postulation -by-symbolization **or** myth

"God" as being or influence directly intuited, or apprehended, subconsciously, non-conceptually; inherited— presuppositional	"God" as consciously imagined, speculatively postulated, mythically symbolized, theoretically explained

1. Common explanatory, symbolic, mythical, theoretical concepts and/or systems:
   animism, polytheism, pantheism, monotheism, deism
   personal, impersonal divinity
   transcendent, immanent
   absolute, infinite, first cause
2. Theoretical, interpretive images and concepts of Christian tradition:
   Creator, Father, King, Judge
   Pre-existent Son of God
   Holy Spirit
   Deus Absconditus (hiding God)
   Deus Revelatus (revealing God)
   Deus Soter (saving God)
   Messiah, Christos
   Omnipotent, omnipresent, omniscient
   Incomprehensible, unchangeable
   Perfect Goodness, Beauty, Truth, Love

Images and concepts such as those of Table IV and other more sophisticated ones that have come and gone.

least within "the community of the faith." As pointed out earlier, the experience and thought of natural science may be symbolized by the word *nature,* and that of religion by the word *God.* But in saying this it should be recognized that in religion the whole experience of the individual as well as the community is so utterly an *experience of God,* and all of religious thought so completely derivative from *thought of God,* that by comparison the importance that attaches to the idea of nature in science—or, for that matter, to any other of the concepts of science—seems secondary and peripheral.

One more introductory remark before we proceed with the analysis: the concept "God" is so utterly different from all others, so completely *sui generis,* in both connotation and existential significance, that anything that may be said about it through the medium of human language is bound to be thoroughly inadequate and in many respects misleading. This should be kept in mind in all discussions of "God," but especially when an *analysis* of the "God" concept is attempted.

2 · THREE COMPONENTS OF THE MEANING OF "GOD"

First I invite detailed attention to Table VI. In column A there are two brief lists, one (A,1) referring to the common experience of mankind that has yielded the universal and perennial concept of "God," and the other (A,2) to the particular experience of the Judaeo-Christian tradition. The latter is divided into (a) its historical and communal aspects, and (b) its personal ones. Column C also has two lists, one (C,1) of various common ways of conceiving the divine for interpretive and explanatory purposes, the other (C,2) of interpretive concepts of Judaeo-Christian thought. In the latter most of the concepts listed are apparently still in good standing; only at the bottom of the list is there reference to such as have come and gone. Column B alludes to the unstructured, intuitive, direct apprehension that leads to deeply felt, presuppositional belief in an "unseen," incomprehensible, yet partly conceivable being, or ground of being. "God B" then symbolizes the non-conceptual ineffability aspect of the reality experienced more conceptually and consciously as "God A," and conceived or postulated in various ways as "God C."

Let us look at each of these three meanings in greater detail.

3 · THE "GOD" CONCEPT-BY-EXPERIENCE

The first column presents then the basic data and facts of religious experience that theology has to work with and endeavors to explain and to interpret. That these represent actual happenings and are therefore factual is attested by the religious community because of what *it* knows experientially. Thus, referring to the common experiences of mankind (A,1), millions of men and women have witnessed to the reality and unique meaningfulness of the experience of "God A" in worship, prayer and symbolic liturgical ritual. For very many of them the phenomena of encounter with the realm of the holy, the *mysterium tremendum et fascinans,* the numinous,* have been quite as real as the encounter with light and electricity—so they would bear witness. As an example of the various aspects of such "awe-full" encounters I have listed the sense of the reality of both sin and righteousness that becomes so overpoweringly convincing in the presence of the Holy One. They are universal phenomena that are experienced by ordinary, normal healthy people of many races and faiths. They cannot be dismissed by the shrug of a shoulder and remarks about fanaticism or mental aberrations.

Referring next to the historical experience of the Judaeo-Christian people (A,2a), the facts to be interpreted by theology are revelational events, each succeeding one of which disclosed another aspect of "God." Here then is a progressive accumulation of factual, experienced *knowledge* of "God A." While these data and facts are different in kind from those of optics, they *are* empirical and in the aggregate constitute quite as impressive a growth of insight as that indicated for light in column A of Table V. Just

---

* If the reader is not familiar with some of these important technical terms, for which no simpler synonyms seem to exist, he is urged to become acquainted with three definitive treatises in this field that have become classics, by Evelyn Underhill, Rudolf Otto, Friedrich Heiler,[1] and more recent ones by Mircea Eliade.[2]

as in Table V there was the progression from rectilinearity of propagation of light to reflection, refraction, diffraction, polarization, so in Table VI there was the progression of the covenanting God, delivering God, the law-giving God and so on.

Now it would appear at first glance that these data are simply historical events in the past, i.e., unrepeated events and therefore not now subject to empirical verification. Actually, however, this is a misconception, for the community considers each of these events as being, in a sense, only the initial disclosure in each case, and that the experience initiated continues.* This means that "God" is experienced as a living God, who today, as much as in Abraham's day, calls men and covenants with his people, who continues to deliver them through exodus from "Egyptian bondage," who continues to be incarnate among them, who continues to conquer sin and take from death its sting, and so on. It is to this ongoing experience of the divine that the community witnesses, as is evidenced again, for instance, in the language of the Statement of Faith of the United Church of Christ, which throughout is predominantly in the present tense. Note there: He seeks, He judges, He bestows, He calls, He promises. There is a confident, knowing, triumphant note there that can come only from what *is* experienced—not only in the past, but in the present.

In such connections as this the question often arises whether there have been any revelational events and experiences in post-biblical time, through which additional facets of the nature of "God" have been disclosed to the Christian community, and whether any others may still be expected. This is a difficult question on which there seems to be no agreement among Christians. Nevertheless I venture to suggest that an affirmative answer may be in order, in the sense that as a matter of fact our conception of God is rather different in important respects from what it was, say, a century or two ago, and that this has not come about simply as a change in thinking per se, but because of what has happened to us, what we have experienced under God. To illustrate, the following

---

* Indeed it might be said that an "event" is itself much more than merely the first historical happening, but rather a whole cluster of happenings then and subsequently. Professor John Knox has developed this point of view with great cogency.[3]

three are concepts-by-experience that constitute added dimensions of our knowledge of God, none of which seem to have been present explicitly in Christian thought to any large extent until relatively recently. The first of these is the concept of a *God of human freedom and equality*. While in the early Church believers were enjoined to accept and love slaves as brothers, no one seemed to understand God's will to be that the institution of slavery should be abolished. Today virtually all Christians would be horrified at the thought that their God is the kind of god who condones slavery as an institution, or has intended some men to be slaves to others. This changed insight has come out of tragic human experiences through which an important aspect of His nature has been disclosed by God and apprehended by man.

A second concept-by-experience that is highly meaningful is the idea of the *God of natural laws* who operates systematically in nature, and in such a way that man can to a significant extent predict and control future physical events. This is an aspect of the "glory of God" that the Psalmist was not aware of, except perhaps only very dimly. This law-and-order concept of God-in-relation-to-nature, and the scientific experience out of which it grew, have profoundly affected Christian thought and experience. In many respects men now pray and worship *differently*, though no less fervently and meaningfully. Gone is the concept of a God of magical tricks, or of a God who has made demons with the power of intervention in nature. Men of faith see new hope for the eradication, under God, of hunger and disease. While there are many unresolved problems in this area of thought about God, there can be no doubt that a new dimension of His nature has been disclosed to the Christian community (and others), and that this did not come primarily from a reorientation of its philosophy, but out of the post-biblical experience of the Church *at work* in the world—and especially scientific work.

Another new concept-by-experience, one closely related to the second, is that of *the creating God*, creating in the present tense. Note again the Statement of Faith: "He calls (not only called) the worlds into being, creates (not only created) man in his own image. . . ." In this case the specific, focusing revelatory event and experience was, it seems to me, the epoch-making disclosure of evolution as a cosmic process. Like all the other great revelatory events in the life of the Judaeo-Christian people, this one was not without intense pain. The insights about God have never come easily, and this one certainly did not.

While I understand that the idea of a God who creates continuously is not new philosophically, it is new empirically, in the sense that not until recently was there empirical evidence that the physical universe has been changing and still is. There had been no compelling reason to suppose that the world did not come into being just a few thousand years ago, and that it has not remained essentially unchanged ever since. Nor was there good reason to suppose that biological species were not fixed and unchanged since they came into being. Now the picture is radically different. Large segments of the Christian Church are convinced that there has been a progressive change in the physical and biological world in many ways and for them this has eventuated in a changed conception of God. If all this makes any sense it is proper to say that the accumulation of our experiential knowledge of "God A" continues and may hopefully be expected to continue.

It is in the light of this continuing, growing, present experience of the community, that the personal experience of the individual, referred to in part 2b of column A, must be understood. It might be thought that much of what appears there should have been classified as common experience and been included in part 1. Christians would say, however, that it is significantly different, different because the Christ experience has given it new meaning and significance. Thus the experience of holy love, of holy awe, of estrangement from man and God, the mystic vision, forgiveness, and so on, all have meaning they did not have before. Indeed to the Christian it seems that through Christ came not only new meaning, but *the* meaning of all that had gone before.

Here then, in column A, resides what succeeding generations of Christians have continued to accept as reliable, permanent, certain and true, and that they never expect to have to unlearn. Here we have the component of the "God" concept that I call the concept-by-experience.

4 · "GOD" CONCEPTS-BY-POSTULATION

In column C we have concepts-by-interpretation and postulation, i.e., the many different ways of thinking about God theoretically. In the first part there are indicated a few of the many radically different systems of thought in terms of which the common religious experience of mankind has been interpreted, e.g., polytheism, pantheism, monotheism, and deism. Then there are the images of God involving such categories as the personal and impersonal, the transcendent and immanent, the absolute and infinite, and others that are more anthropomorphic (and justifiably so), such as king, judge, and father.

Passing to part 2, we again note the effect of the Christ experience upon the community, this time upon its formal, interpretive thinking about God. Out of this Christ-illuminated thinking there came eventually a whole series of new theological terms and concepts, such as the Godhead, the Trinity, the pre-existent Son of God, the Holy Spirit, Deus Absconditus, Deus Revelatus, omnipotence, omnipresence, omniscience, perfect goodness, perfect truth, *agape,* grace, providence, the wholly other, and many others. These became necessary because Christians found it impossible with the old vocabulary to tell adequately all there was to tell, to interpret all that had been and was being experienced. They had been "born again," and a "new being" had been created. Life had new dimensions. Therefore new modes of thought and explanation simply had to be devised.

To illustrate this a bit more concretely, let us ask just why some of these new theological terms did seem necessary. Referring for a moment to the analogous question in science, I feel as a science teacher that whenever a theoretical concept is introduced in, say, a physics course, the student should be encouraged to ask immediately why this is being done. What is there in the empirical situation that makes that particular concept desirable? In other words, every such concept should be anchored explicitly to an empirical situation in which it is expected to be useful. Why, for instance, *should* or can we think of light in terms of wave properties? Why ascribe (postulate) wave characteristics to atoms, especially if we have been thinking of them for good reasons as particles? Why think of heat and temperature in terms of the motion and kinetic energy of molecules? I feel that similarly every effort should be made explicitly to relate theological concepts to the empirical religious situation.

The question is then why, for example, the concepts of omnipotence and omnipresence were postulated as characteristics of God. Conceivably, of course, this might be answered metaphysically in terms of attributes that *should* go with an a-priori conception of God. But this is not what we want to know. More specifically then, what was there about the God-experience of the early Christians—or the later ones for that matter—that called for these concepts?

The answer at least in part seems to be that by postulating omnipotence as a quality of God one can explain the experience of the Christian Church that no matter how desperate the plight in which God's grace and help is needed, no matter how serious the difficulty or danger from which the Christian needs to be extricated, no matter how tremendous the task to be performed, God is able to provide the necessary aid and succor. If men need daily bread, or power to withstand "the fiery darts of the devil," God can provide it. Jesus was raised from the dead. Sin was conquered. Nothing is impossible to God. This is the experiential meaning of *omnipotence*. And in the early Church this was no mere academic question, for in those days many men worshipped gods whom they did not consider to be omnipotent.

Omnipresence? Wherever a man is, there God is also. Moreover, however far the community of the faith was scattered throughout the earth at any time, God was still experienced by each of its members. Furthermore, if one tried to escape from God's searching presence, however far, He was still there. He is everywhere. To this the Christian experience has always testified, and theology recognizes this with the postulated concept of the divine attribute of omnipresence.

Why the strange sounding concept of the Deus Absconditus, the idea of the God who *seems* at times to withdraw or absent Himself from men but who is rather in mercy only veiling or hiding Himself? It enables theology to explain, at least to a degree, two very real human experiences, to which many Christians have testified. The first is that all men of faith feel at times to be forgotten or forsaken by God, when their prayers seem to remain unanswered or even unheard, when it seems that there may not even be a God. The second is the awe-full, overpowering, blinding impact of the presence or view of God—when men cry out that this is more than they can bear. Where can they hide from this penetrating and consuming radiance? This is a well known experience.

God is for Christianity, as well as for other religions, the God of light, the light that both illumines, enlightens and energizes, and searches out, penetrates and exposes. His light is so intense as to be overpowering, consuming and blinding, and yet it may be gently warming, softly glowing and beneficently healing. At times a man cannot endure as much light upon him as at others, and sometimes he needs much more. The Christian conception is that God never actually departs from or forsakes men. He is ever present. But He does hide behind a veil, sometimes many folds of it and sometimes few—thus shedding more, or less, light upon men, according to their varying needs. If God did not thus veil himself no one could stand in His presence, and if He did not unveil Himself, no one would ever see Him, and men would be in perpetual darkness.

This is, of course, highly symbolic language and imagery, but that it is not mere fancy is attested by actual experience that makes it truly meaningful. It is analogous to the problem of trying to see what the surface of the sun looks like, and to observe the so-called sun spots. If one looked directly at the sun, one would be blinded. One way to proceed is to look through a blackened photographic film or smoked glass. This protects the eyes and yet enables one to see the spots clearly. Thus it is with "seeing" God. His veiling Himself to men is making Himself discernible. So says Christian experience; and so interprets Christian theology through its concept of the Deus Absconditus.[4]

Let us in this connection consider, and apply this method to, a few concepts that are not God-concepts themselves. First, the puzzling concept of *original sin,* and that of *sin* itself without the adjective. Why not simply the more common notions of evil or unethical conduct? The answer is that for the Christian community sin and unethical conduct are not at all synonymous—though they are, of course, related. Experientially they are vastly different both in magnitude (enormity) and kind. Sin in its primary meaning is estrangement and separation from, or at times even outright rebellion against, God, whereas unethical conduct is basically violation of a code. Hence the need for the religious concept of *sin,* as distinct from the related ones of ethics.

More than that, however, the community has needed also the concept of *original sin,* to denote man's seemingly compelling tendency toward sin. Concerning this I should like to quote from a remarkable book, entitled *Doctrine in the Church of England.* It is the report of the Commission on Christian Doctrine (twenty-five members), appointed by the Archbishops of Canterbury and York in 1922, and published in 1938. This is not formally a treatise on theology, but a book for the common reader that has much fine theology in it. The following quotation is from the section entitled "The Fact of Sin."

> It is a fact of experience that man is prone to sin. This is not to be understood to mean that man is 'totally depraved', or is not also prone in many ways to righteousness. What is affirmed is that every man does in fact tend, in one respect or another, to be and to do what is other than perfectly good. This is, indeed, a grave understatement of the reality of human evil. . . .
>
> The term 'original sin' is to some extent ambiguous. It stands for the sinful disposition which is in fact found in all men from a time apparently previous to any responsible act of choice; but historically it has been associated with an interpretation of this which refers it to the transgression of the first man. In any case the fact demands explanation, for it seems to reflect discredit upon the Creator. . . .
>
> Among the historic attempts in Christian theology to explain man's sinful disposition, three streams of thought are of special importance. These may be indicated by the following phrases: (a) Loss of communion with God; (b) racial depravity and guilt; (c) modern evolutionary theories. Each of these draws attention to important elements of the truth: (a) Our sinful state cannot be rightly estimated except in connection with man's relation to God; (b) there is a solidarity of the race in sin as in redemption; (c) original sin must be related to our evolutionary inheritance. . . .[5]

Aside from shedding light upon the idea of original sin, this quotation illustrates three aspects of much of recent theological thinking. First, fact and interpretation are carefully differentiated, and interpretation is indeed anchored in experience. Second, some of the recognized purposes of interpretive theory are to explain experience, to account for puzzling phenomena, and to resolve perplexity due to apparently paradoxical interpretations. Third, scientific concepts are definitely reckoned with in theological theorizing, in this case evolutionary concepts.

In column C we have indicated then a number of concepts-by-postulation, i.e., thought patterns and concepts of interpretation. As pointed out earlier, here resides not permanent truth, but transient usefulness of interpretation, and it is here that we should expect, and be prepared to accept, change as time goes on. There is, however, another aspect of the matter, namely that it is in this realm of interpretation that Christians tend to disagree and develop controversy. This too is to be expected. To illustrate this I quote again from the Anglican book—and the discussion of original sin. It is worth noting that this is a pronouncement by a group of scholar-churchmen who carried on intimate, critical discussion for fifteen years before issuing a report.

> We are agreed in asserting that man, as known to history, both now and throughout the ages, has been under the influence of a bias toward evil.
> In our interpretation of this fact, and in relating it to the purpose of God we are not agreed.[6]

The Report then goes on to delineate their differences. On some aspects of the subject there are as many as four different interpretations. Notice that the disagreements pertain to the theoretical considerations, not to the facts of the case. This is not to discount theoretical thinking, but only to say that here is where there is the elasticity that is needed to allow for both differences and change.

There are those who object to the use of the term "theoretical" with reference to theological interpretations. This is hard to understand, for it seems evident that in fact theological interpretations do function as theories. Many theologians not only acknowledge this, but definitely assert it. Thus the members of this commission have this to say on the subject:

The fulness of the Divine life revealed in Christ cannot be adequately expressed in human language, and *theological statements share the limitations of all theoretical formulae*. It must be recognized that changes in forms of thought and the progress of knowledge may necessitate changes in the intellectual formulation of the content of Revelation, though this does not mean that there is any change in that which has been revealed. The apprehension of Revelation by the human mind must needs find expression in the form of propositions, but no such formulations are to be regarded as being in principle irreformable. It may be that there are theological propositions accepted in the Church which will always be found neither to need nor to be capable of revision, and in that sense may be 'final'; if so, they are not final in the sense that they are exempt from examination but in the sense that examination invariably leads to their re-affirmation [7] (italics mine).

Note the term "theoretical" in this passage, as well as the open-minded attitude and methodological point of view that accompanies it. This is evident again in the next quotation, where we find the term "speculative theology" in a discussion of the Eucharist.

The history of Eucharistic doctrine has been marked by two stages which are significant in this connection. For about eight hundred years the attempt to understand and to express precisely how the Gift is given, and to provide an account of the Gift in its various relations, was subordinate to a thankful recognition of the reality of the Gift itself. . . . The spiritual enjoyment of the heavenly food of the Lord's Body and Blood in the life of the Church was the dominant fact; questions of speculative theology remained in the background.

There then followed a stage of definition and controversy, beginning in the ninth century, and marked by attempts at precision. . . .

No Christian doubts that in some sense Christ is present in the Holy Communion. But the use of the words 'present' and 'presence' gives rise to many questions, and has led to deep divisions of thought and of devotional practice among Christians.[8]

Observe again the clear differentiation between experiential fact and interpretive theory, and the recognition of the former as the locus of agreement and the latter of disagreement.

It should be noted that in this section we have, for the most part, considered concepts whose experiential and interpretive components could be separated rather easily, so that it made sense to talk as though facts and interpretations were sharply distinguishable. As we observed earlier, some facts are relatively much less heavily laden with theoretical elements than others. This is the case for most of these particular concepts. In religious, as in scientific, thought, there are many situations where it is altogether proper to say that *this* is fact and *that* is theory—even though this does involve slight oversimplification. In the main this is the kind of situation we have dealt with in this section.

5 · THE "GOD" CONCEPT-BY-INTUITION OR -BY-PRESUPPOSITION

The heading of column B of Table VI includes the two terms intuition and presupposition—as does the title above. This is because they are closely related. As we shall see in the next chapter, presuppositions, like concepts, are of various types and have multiple meanings and origins. Those of interest to us now have a dual origin, first in direct intuitive apprehension and the primal, subconscious awareness and visceral thinking that I have referred to as "feeling it in one's bones," and, second, in communal and cultural inheritance and conditioning. It is in this dual sense that the concept presupposition is used here. It does not refer to deliberate assumptions or postulations laid down in advance as a foundation for a syllogistic train of thought. Column B refers neither to deliberate postulation nor to historical experience, but to more ineffable, nonconceptual aspects of man's encounter with God and therefore of his "knowledge" of God. This is why this column is, unlike the other two, empty—except for its brief characterizing heading. There is very little that can be put into words. Though this is not to say that it is meaningless or irrelevant.

Obviously then we are back again to the "God above the God of theism," i.e., above both the abstract intellectual postulations symbolized by "God C" and the more concrete experiences represented by "God A," the God who is never "seen," but who shows Himself, who is forever "unknown" and yet "makes Himself known," who is both conceivable and inconceivable, who, in short, defies all attempts to grasp Him intellectually or otherwise, and yet who grasps anyone with ultimate concern. We are back to the God who can be met, loved, obeyed, and trusted—though not comprehended.

But no man ever apprehends or intuits God in a vacuum or in complete solitude. Always such apprehension becomes possible, at least in part, because of predispositions, as well as preconceptions and beliefs, mediated by community and culture. Unfortunately, the human capacity for intuition seems not to have been studied very extensively in the West. Indeed the mention of it usually raises skeptical questions more than it provides enlightenment. I venture to suggest, however, that critical investigation of it will eventually reveal an interesting and perhaps circular interrelationship between individual and communal intuition, on the one hand, and cultural presuppositions on the other. It may be that "God B" can be apprehended intuitively only because of presuppositional beliefs that exist in community and culture, *and* that in turn those beliefs exist largely because of intuitive apprehension. Logically this circularity is not very satisfactory; but perhaps this is not actually important. Probably we have a great deal to learn here from the East.

Incidentally, it may be remarked also that the foundations of intuitive insight in religion may not be very different from those underlying science.

Now then, to sum up what has been developed thus far in this chapter, it seems that if asked what the symbol "God" denotes, one might well say that it symbolizes God experienced, God postulated and God intuitively apprehended and presupposed. It symbolizes factual truth, illuminating interpretation, and intuitive and inherited insight. From the viewpoint of the Christian community, all this together constitutes its "knowledge" of God—and all of it comes about because God by grace discloses Himself in what it calls divine revelation.

In what sense is such knowledge verifiable, if at all?

6 · VERIFICATION AND PROOF

For Christianity, reliability of experience and knowledge is quite as important as for science, and illusion or delusion quite as disastrous. Therefore it is vitally interested in authentication and verification. How does it achieve them? By *essentially* the same processes, I think, as science employs. This means that in religion too the problem and method of verification must necessarily be different respectively for the three kinds of assertions associated with the three classes of concepts to which we have given special attention. What must be established for them respectively is that they be reliably true, reliably interpretive and explanatory, and reliably intuitive and presuppositional.

In the case of a statement involving a concept-by-experience, i.e., one claiming that something has actually happened and been experienced, on what basis does the Christian community accept it as true? Upon the same basis as the science community does, namely (a) that the happening has been experienced by several individuals or by the community as a whole, and not only by one individual, and (b) that it is experientially and theoretically consistent with what is already accepted as known.

When a new theological theory is up for consideration, and an interpretive, explanatory statement is made on the basis of it, how is it validated? I think both history and present practice show that this is achieved in two steps. First, assuming that it meets the criteria of internal excellence, such as logical self-consistency, intelligibility and simplicity, it may be validated externally by checking against the empirical data, to test on the one hand its explanatory and descriptive power, and on the other hand its fertility. Second, it must be shown that it fits into the current theoretical scheme of things, or, if not, provides a new general interpretive scheme.

Thinking of the first step, the history of Christian doctrine exhibits many cases of proposed concepts-by-postulation and theological theories that were rejected because they were not consistent with the facts of experience. Some of the theories of the nature of Jesus Christ, for example, conceived of Him as essentially God in human guise. These have been rejected consistently on the ground that Jesus was experientially known to be in every respect a man. Similarly theories as to the nature of man are rejected when they disregard or contradict what the Church regards as fact, e.g., original sin. One test of a theological theory is then that it must not violate the known facts.

This first step includes also a checking of a theory or concept-by-postulation relative to its fertility, i.e., its power to lead the community into new insights and new experiences, and thus to enrich and extend its work and thought. On this basis a theoretical idea is to be rejected if it impoverishes the religious life of the Church, by impairing its spiritual sensitivity, stifling its thinking, paralyzing its transformative action in the world. Thus if a new "God" concept-by-postulation were to lead to less love of God and of neighbor, or to an inability any longer to distinguish between good and evil, it would face rejection.

This criterion is obviously somewhat like the scientific one of fertility and predictability, which demands that a new theoretical idea shall lead to more research and therefore to new empirical knowledge, to new theoretical ideas, and thus to the enrichment of the communal life and work, i.e., to the advancement of science. Clearly in the more restricted sense of the word *prediction,* namely predicting what particular values a certain variable would have under given conditions, or predicting that a new phenomenon would be observed if looked for under certain conditions, there is in religion no prediction by theological theory. If, on the other hand, the broader notion of prediction and fertility is adopted as a criterion of acceptability, then we can say—without stretching the point too far—that *in principle* scientific and theological theories must meet the same criteria when they are checked in terms of their strategic usefulness or effects.

The second step in the validation of theories in religion calls for establishing their consistency with other theories. Here too the history of doctrine provides many examples of interpretations that did not gain acceptance because they created more problems than they solved, since they were inconsistent with others and yet provided no new perspective by which they could be reconciled. The theory of the Trinity is an example of a concept that was successful in this regard, though it required about three hundred years before it was formulated satisfactorily.

A feature of the validation of theological theory that distinguishes it from the scientific case is that it usually takes much longer to achieve it. This is understandable, since in religion concepts-by-postulation are not quantitative, are less capable of precise formulation, are much more complex in content, and far more consequential in personal life. Therefore both the correspondence between theoretical interpretation and empirical fact, and the consistency or inconsistency of interpretations, are much more difficult to establish. For the application of the fertility-prediction criterion usually requires a long time, since the effect of a particular theory may show up but slowly and even then cannot be evaluated easily.

Moreover, there is in religion a disturbing factor virtually nonexistent in natural science, though it is certainly in evidence in social science. We have emphasized that in science and religion there is always interaction between theory and data, that there are no bare facts, and that one's observations and experiments, and even the various kinds of verification, are always affected by one's modes of thought and one's theoretical perspectives. In religion, however, as in social science, there is another interaction effect, namely that *the data themselves* may be changed profoundly by theory, so that what is to be interpreted is itself modified by the very process of developing or applying the interpretation. To illustrate, suppose the community is a fervently praying community, and a theory of God is then developed and tentatively accepted which interprets Him as not wanting prayers. Without doubt the community would soon cease to be a praying one, a new experience pattern would have appeared, and the original one that yielded the data would have disappeared or been radically altered. I am not at the moment raising the question of whether this would be desirable or not, but am simply pointing out an important effect that apparently is not operative in natural science in any marked degree. It is obvious, however, that the effect complicates the problem and method of validation—though probably not fatally.

As we turn to the question of verification in the realm of concepts-by-presupposition, we encounter a situation very much like that of the corresponding scientific case. How is it possible to verify the assertion that "God B" exists, or that God makes His presence felt to man, or that an individual may know that he is in the presence of God? For one thing, no one claims that God exists in the sense that a house or barn does, nor even in the sense that light does. And yet the nature of religion, certainly that of the Christian faith, is such that the community testifies that He reveals Himself, loves, calls, promises, redeems, and that His presence may be known in the living faith relationship. The only validation of such claims, in so far as they result from direct apprehension or awareness of God ("God B"), is, as I see it, that of communal consensus, intersubjective cross-checking, sharing.

Is God real? We know—if we know anything at all—the actuality in experience of what the symbol "God A" stands for. We know also the actuality in our minds of the postulations the symbol "God C" denotes. We can validate these in the manner indicated earlier. But does the God of "God B" have actuality? It is doubtful that this question has an answer of the type many persons would desire. Probably it can be answered only in an existential mood of personal involvement and of ultimate concern, never in a mood of sheer curiosity. To the curiosity kind of question there is no adequate answer in this case. If, on the other hand, the question comes from deep, anxious concern as to what God may mean in one's own life, and how one should relate oneself to Him, then one has already become aware of Him.

At any rate religion seemingly does not claim to be able to verify the reliability of a concept-by-presupposition, certainly not any more than science does—*except,* to use the suggestive Latin phrase that applies here, by *consensus communis fidelium.*

Now a few words about the word *proof* that occurs in the title of this section of the chapter. What is it that people want when they call for *proof* of a belief? Do they mean the removal of all possibility of doubt by some sort of inerrant logical device? If so, this is a forlorn hope, for there is no such possibility. In the chapter on the permanence and transience of scientific and religious knowledge, certainty has been claimed for experienced knowledge in both realms. This is a certainty that one depends upon, builds on, that satisfies the scientific and religious communities, and enables one generation to accept with confidence what it inherits from its predecessors. But, alas, it is not the kind that can satisfy him who demands that all possible doubt be removed.

7 · OTHER CONCEPTS

As in the case of science, most concepts of religion have only two components, the empirical and theoretical ones. Certainly this is true of such as omniscience, sin, righteousness, grace, providence, revelation, redemption, salvation, justification, sanctification, atonement, incarnation, resurrection, ascension. It is important to understand that all these concepts are based in experience, in the broad, inclusive, many-sided sense of "experience" that I have indicated in Chapter V. Especially I refer to communal experience—which includes personal experience—both past and present. Altogether too often the uninformed throw up their hands in horror at theological concepts, feeling that they represent meaningless abstractions far removed from actual living. Intellectual honesty demands, however, that before such terms are dismissed out of hand they be looked at carefully as to their *actual* meanings and origins. If this be done, most theological terms, certainly the most important ones, will be seen to come from very real human experiences and urgent concerns and to make a great deal of sense.

Take for instance the perplexing concept of *miracle*. One reason why it is so puzzling is that, while it is a religious term, it is commonly defined negatively and at least partially in terms of scientific categories, as when it is said to be a *violation* or *suspension* of natural law. Now this approach is unfortunate for three reasons. First, such a definition is clearly only theoretical and interpretive, and therefore can at most represent only the postulational component of the concept. Second, as a postulational definition it is unsatisfactory because it thoroughly misrepresents much of contemporary theological thought on the subject. Thus few, if any, Protestant theologians think of miracles in that way today. Third, it fails utterly to convey the religious meaning of the concept *miracle,* and instead sets up a non-religious problem where there actually may be none in the first place. It gives no hint that the concept is empirical in origin and comes out of existential situations marked by deep, ultimate, rather than magical, concern.

I suggest therefore that in this case a better approach to understanding is to start with a concept-by-experience. From this point of view a miracle is said to be an event in which God is "seen" to be working out his purpose of love and redemption in an especially wonderful, mysterious, and yet convincing way. While there is in the Church much disagreement about miracles as defined theoretically, there is none, so far as I am aware, about their reality and meaningfulness in this religiously empirical sense. To illustrate, for the Christian tradition the great epoch-making miracles were the Exodus, when Israel was delivered fom Egyptian bondage, and the event of the Christ, when the bondage of sin was broken and a "new creation" was brought into being. Within the Church there is no doubt that they actually happened, and that they happened at critical times when the need for God's action in the life of "His people" and the world was especially urgent. They illustrate also the significant fact that for faith a genuine miracle is always a truly revelatory event, disclosing the love and will of God, never a merely magical display of power or authority for its own sake.[9] And it underscores another fact, namely, that theological concepts are not usually abstractions far removed from life, but have their origin in truly human and existentially significant problems and situations.

There have been many attempts to explain miracles, i.e., to construct theories of how God can or does perform them. The idea that miracles constitute divine suspensions of natural law is only one such theory.[10] None, however, seems to enjoy universal acceptance in the Church today. We have here then a concept which is typical of many others in both religion and science, which, though they certainly have two components, can clearly be defined at the time only in terms of the one, the component-by-experience. In such cases the only course open to us is to await further theoretical or interpretational developments until an adequate concept-by-postulation makes its appearance and passes muster.*

Let us look at three other examples. In the total Christ event there were, of course, particular miracles. Three of these have seemed to the Church to be especially meaningful, namely the *incarnation,* the *resurrection,* and the *coming of the Holy Spirit* at Pentecost. All three of them are extremely difficult to understand if approached from the theoretical or postulational side. They seem much less so from the viewpoint of the actual experience of the Christian community. Thus *incarnation* means the coming of God among men, especially in Jesus experienced as the Christ. The *resurrection of Christ* means that after He died and was buried He reappeared alive to the community in some real experiential form.

---

*There are of course also concepts that have been developed theoretically before there has been the corresponding empirical discovery.

The *coming of the Holy Spirit* means that at Pentecost spiritual forces were released in unprecedented manner, and that Peter and his fellows were given a vision of their mission, and power for the tasks ahead. However these mighty, miraculous experiences may be portrayed and explained theoretically, their basic meaning resides in what the community actually knows took place—though it may not know how it came about. Here is where the Church can and should make its truth-claims regarding miracles.

As for the corresponding concepts-by-postulation, this is another matter, and calls for much more conservative claims. To ask just what happened in the resurrection in terms of physical categories, e.g., whether the resurrected body of Christ was composed of molecules or not, is to enter the realm of speculation and hypothesis, where truth-claims cannot be made. The same would be true of any attempts to inquire into what went on physically, in terms of cause-and-effect relations, when the Israelites crossed the Red Sea. The fact is that we do not know. Any answer would have to be theoretical. And no adequate theory exists.

There are also many miracle stories that do not have the same epoch-making momentous religious significance as do those we have considered thus far. Examples come to mind easily: Moses' "miraculous" rod that became a serpent and then a rod again, his hand that became leprous and then was immediately healed again, the sun that stood still, the ax that floated, the water that turned into wine, the walking on water, the calming of a storm by word of mouth, and many others. We need not enter into a detailed discussion of these, since our main purpose is to study the more general question of the nature of religious concepts, and of the attitude and methodology of the religious community relative to them. Suffice it then to say that the Church has become rather wary of miracles. Most theologians would agree that miracle stories should be subjected to very careful and critical scrutiny before being accepted, and that each one should be analyzed from two points of view, the experiential and the interpretive.

With regard to the factual aspect, two distinctly different questions arise. Did the alleged event really take place? And if so, was it a miracle? Any proposed answers to these two questions must be subjected to the appropriate verification and validation procedures, such as we have already studied. This means that with regard to the first question, that of historical factuality, a miracle story is to be treated no differently from any other. In the case of an ancient miracle, for instance, this becomes admittedly a very difficult undertaking, and may raise serious doubt as to its authenticity. From this there is no escape. As to the second question, it should be clear that no amount of purely historical or scientific evidence that might be marshalled is competent to establish that a given event was a miracle. Even if photographic and other scientifically admissible evidence had been produced that persons had actually walked on water across a lake, this would not prove that a miracle had occurred. For this in itself would not establish that God had been "working out his purpose of love and redemption in an especially wonderful, mysterious, and convincing way." Indeed, if such an event were actually authenticated physically, the scientists would quite properly go to work at once, if interested, to see how this event could be fitted into the over-all cause-and-effect scheme of things. Perhaps some new kind of physical force would have to be postulated by which the phenomenon could be explained. In any case, whether science could or could not succeed in finding an explanation would have no bearing on whether the happening should or should not be recognized as a miracle. This is a religious question that can be answered only religiously. It is in this spirit that contemporary scholarship handles the conceptual and cognitive problem of miracles—and all other difficult concepts. As a result, many of the miracle stories no longer seem acceptable, while others are. What needs to be emphasized especially—if this discussion is to contribute to our understanding of the nature of religion and religious thought—is that a miracle is a religious category, and that an event, be it ordinary or extraordinary from a nonreligious point of view, can be seen to be divinely miraculous only through the eye of faith. To anyone without such faith no event is divinely miraculous.

8 · COGNITION; THE PUBLIC AND PRIVATE DOMAINS

While nothing has been demonstrated beyond question in this brief discussion, there has emerged a picture of the remarkable similarity with regard to cognition in the realms of religion and science.

More specifically, the assertion by Professor Williams seems to be vindicated, to the effect that "All knowledge without exception is derived from a critical interpretation of what is given in human experience." True, what is known in science and religion respectively is to a large extent very different. Nevertheless in both, the claim of knowledge is based on what has been experienced, and critically analyzed and interpreted. Granted that the specific techniques of perception, analysis, verification and validation are different in detail, they are nevertheless similar in principle, so much so, I think, that when subjected to an analysis and test of their adequacy they must stand or fall together.

A parenthetical remark about revelation may be in order here. In accepting Professor Williams' dictum we are not losing sight of divine revelation—any more than he has. It was his potent definition that was quoted in the third chapter: "To speak of revelation in the prophets and Christ . . . is to speak of those happenings in human history which have so opened our eyes and so transformed our minds that the disclosure of God to man has taken place." Professor H. Richard Niebuhr puts it this way: "When we speak of revelation we mean that something has happened to us in our history which conditions all our thinking and that through this happening we are enabled to apprehend. . . . We mean that something has happened which compels our faith and which requires us to seek rationality and unity in the whole of our history. . . . In dealing with revelation we refer to something in our history to which we always return as containing our first certainty." [11] The concept of revelation has to do with the most actual of actual happenings and experiences, and the most demanding of demanding quests for rational interpretation. It is not a process to be thought of as an extrasensory perception, or as requiring a transrational or subrational organ especially provided by the Creator for the gaining of religious knowledge, or for the hearing of words spoken by God in some supra-acoustical or exclusively mystical manner.

So understood, a belief in the reality of revelation as God's self-disclosure does not, it seems to me, invalidate the proposition that religious knowledge comes out of experience critically interpreted—and the proposition that the scientific and religious cognitive processes are in principle similar.

In both science and religion the claim is made that knowledge is communicable and intelligible intersubjectively. Therefore both operate in the public domain—at least the domain that is in each case public to a large community of individuals. In both, the exigencies of life make it necessary for any individual to accept much knowledge on trust from his fellows. No individual can possibly experience everything, or verify all claims himself. And yet in neither is an individual expected to accept belief blindly without convincing *himself* that it is reasonable to do so, on the basis of empirical evidence and critical analysis. By *empirical evidence* is meant in this connection the evidence available to him personally from his own limited experience, as well as the more extensive experiential or historical evidence reported by other members of the community, either past or present. Thus in both science and religion knowledge is achieved by a combination of individual and communal perception and theoretical interpretation. Neither is utterly individualistic or completely communal.

To speak of the "private domain" in this connection seems to me to be neither helpful nor relevant. It is, of course, true that every person has his own experiences in his own private domain —in both science and religion—and that this experience has for him unique significance and to some extent probably even unique content. Thus a man's perception of the color *blue,* his own hearing of a symphony, his love for a particular woman, his hatred of a favorite enemy, or his own religious rebirth, are certainly likely to be unique in many ways. But they are also in many respects typical, and therefore do not call for unique concepts or meanings; and they do not constitute additions to religious or scientific knowledge or insight. Hence for present purposes reference to the private domain is not relevant; and to assert, as it is often asserted, that scientific knowledge pertains to the public domain and that the religious is private, is downright erroneous.

9 · MOODS OF DIFFIDENCE AND CONFIDENCE

In discussing certain aspects of contemporary science we noted an increasingly renunciatory attitude toward theory and a hesitancy in regard to making claims as to the "reality" of "unseen entities" such as photons, electrons, and the so-called elementary particles. There is abroad in the science community a growing diffidence about pressing questions about existence and reality too far, and a humble recognition that the methods and resources of science may not be all-powerful and self-sufficient, and that after all, in addition to the unknown still to be conquered, there may be a realm altogether unknowable to science. We would not be describing the nature of religion adequately if we did not note similar, though more intense, moods and feelings in that field, especially in Judaism and Christianity.

In an important sense the kind of thinking that appears in this chapter is not consonant with that found in the Bible. I refer to the analysis of the God concept. One of the remarkable features of that collection of writings called the Bible, produced by many authors of different temperaments, times and cultural backgrounds, is the unanimity of their reticence * to speak about the nature of God, to say anything about Him except in terms of His actions and deeds, or even only to mention Him by any name whatsoever. Moreover, one looks in vain for any attempt to formulate a concept of God or to *analyze* it. Indeed in the second commandment of the decalogue we have a prohibition against "imaging" God, which the Jewish community seems to have taken much more seriously than has the Christian. There is in the history of Christian doctrine unmistakable evidence of a perennial tension between the desire to define "God" carefully and precisely in order to rule out misconception and error, and the fear that if He were defined, He would be misrepresented thereby, or even be displaced in men's hearts and minds by their inadequate images of Him. For many centuries the desire to define prevailed, and consequently creeds, catechisms and theology tended to become more and more detailed in their metaphysical specification of God. More recently, however, there has been a strong reaction against this, and the fear of philosophic images has gained the ascendancy. Consequently creedal statements, together with theology, have tended to become more simply confessional, without the metaphysical trappings, more like the venerable Apostles' Creed and the Statement of Faith to which we have referred repeatedly.

There is then abroad in the Church a gratifying growing dif-

---

* This striking reticence in the Bible was called to my attention first some years ago by my brother, Dr. Frederick A. Schilling, able theologian and clergyman.

fidence about pressing certain theological questions too far, and a refreshingly humble doubt as to the complete adequacy or self-sufficiency of theology's methods and resources. It is less eager to assert that it knows just how God operates in the world, or even what His will and demands are in specific situations. If this be true, it says much that is gratifying about contemporary Christian thought.

Along with this growing reticence, there is evident in the religious community an increasing confidence that for the most part religious thought and theology are on the right track methodologically. Both science and religion are of such a nature that they have not been overly concerned about justifying their conceptualizing and cognitive processes. Both have considered it more important to get on with their main business, while simply taking it for granted confidently that mankind is so equipped and constituted, that much scientific and religious knowledge can be attained reliably and meaningfully by the processes in hand. Confidence in this assumption is, in my opinion, increasing, even though its validity has not been *established*—and perhaps never can be.

10 · A CONCLUDING DEMURRER

In certain respects these two chapters on concepts are likely to be misleading with regard to both science and religion. They may give the impression that the development of concepts and meanings proceeds rectilinearly by straightforward logic, after the manner of Fig. 1(a).* They may suggest that experience and theory are in practice related in a columnar or pyramidal manner, with experience always being prerequisite to theory both logically and chronologically. They may imply that the separation of meaning-by-experience, meaning-by-intuition or -presupposition, and meaning-by-postulation, is inevitably clear-cut and obvious, and that the various verification and validation processes are always deliberately sequential and convincingly crucial. But *none of this is intended, for none of it would be true.* Things appear that way only by hindsight. Actually in the historic—or, shall we say, the frontier—situation, concepts form slowly and circuitously, insight

* See diagram, p. 34.

comes painfully, and meanings are in perpetual flux and modification. While the distinctions and separations made in our analysis are accurate as first approximations, they are also to some extent oversimplifications. As to the way concepts develop, we should remember and reaffirm the circularity and perpetual interaction of experience and theory, and the essentially non-logical character of much scientific and religious thought.

Moreover, with respect to religion in particular, it must be emphasized that basic meanings come out of the existential situation more than out of deliberate ivory-tower reasoning. Concepts are fashioned out of faith and doubt, anxiety and hope, love and hate, triumphs and defeats, that constitute man's struggle under God for truth and righteousness. They accompany the efforts of men under God to conquer disease and famine, to bring about social justice, and to eliminate war. Under such conditions ideas and meanings, differences and distinctions, truth and error, are never clear-cut, and particular methods never quite adequate or appropriate. And yet withal, insight and knowledge do emerge. And when looked at in retrospect, they are seen to have come out of individual and communal faith and reason, experience and interpretation, in a powerfully effective, indissoluble, circular interdependence and unity. There is but one cognition—though it is compounded of many different constituent elements.

CHAPTER X

Interrelations and Interactions Among Concepts

And Cultural Influences

1 · A DIFFERENT LOOK AT SCIENTIFIC METHOD

Let us now return to the subject of methodology and look at it from a somewhat different point of view. I have said that science has many methods, not one, that there is no such thing as "the scientific method" as this is popularly conceived, i.e., as a sort of step-by-step guide on what-to-do-next when carrying on an investigation. Indeed we have said that what is different or unique about science must be ascribed in the main to the uniqueness of its subject matter, rather than to any distinctiveness of method itself. Scientific method is then no more than the application or adaptation of the general methods of intelligence to those problems or aspects of the world in which science is especially interested.

For a long time it was customary to describe scientific method almost exclusively in terms of the general processes of observation, induction, deduction and experimental verification. This certainly looked like a neat scheme of definite steps. It was commonly thought of as an inductive ascent from the particulars of raw data to a generalization, followed by a deductive descent from the generalization back again to the particulars of experimentation. This scheme had, of course, much to commend it. For one thing it did place emphasis upon the empirical foundation of science, which is, of course, a proper emphasis—as long as it is not an *over*emphasis. It stressed the fact that science answers its questions about nature by appealing directly to nature itself rather than to metaphysical systems, and that scientific "proof" does not consist of logical deduction from a-priori assumptions. In the early history of science, when scientific patterns of thought were just coming into their own, this emphasis was especially desirable—even necessary. It was important also in the days of controversy over such questions as the structure of the heavens, and the age and evolution of the earth. To gain knowledge in geology and astronomy one must address one's questions to the earth and the stars, not the Bible. The final court of appeal must be observation and experiment.

Unfortunately, when one emphasizes one aspect of a subject one is in danger of de-emphasizing others, or even of creating wrong impressions altogether. And this is exactly what has happened. This picture of inductive ascent and deductive descent, the one beginning with and the other ending with "facts," has created the impression that what science is interested in most of all is data and facts, whereas this certainly is not the case.

Now, in recent years interpreters of science have tended to shift this emphasis and to stress instead the importance, if not the primacy, of concepts rather than data or even "facts," hence scientific method has come to be described schematically in other ways. One of the most helpful and best known diagrams depicting this newer approach has been devised by Professor Henry Margenau of Yale. It has been referred to by many authors and employed for the clarification of many ideas. Margenau himself has used it with reference not only to science [1] itself, but to ethics and to religion.[2] Such a diagram is presented as Fig. 3. With apologies to its originator, I have taken certain liberties with it by adding a few features.

The vertical line is called the perceptual plane, or simply the P-plane. Without signifying any commitment to a particular psychological doctrine, it simply stands for the human experience of perception. Nature, to the left of the P-plane, somehow impinges upon human consciousness so that one becomes aware of sounds, sights, smells and tastes of various sorts, of smooth and rough surfaces, sharp and blunt edges, or pulls and pushes, and many other percepts. Thus there appear on the P-plane the data of experience, represented in the diagram by the x's.

The circles stand for concepts. They are imbedded in what

Margenau calls the C-field. This is the cognitive field or the realm of thought, i.e., of reason, reflection, selection, analysis, synthesis, abstraction, and so on. The data (x's) are imposed upon experience by nature. They are given and intractable, and in no sense created by the observer. But the concepts are constructed by the mind, and may be called *constructs*. All of them are interrelated by reason, by logical and sometimes mathematical rules. This is indicated by the lines connecting the circles. If one were to analyze a particular concept one might find it definable at least in part in terms of a neighboring one to the left, and this by means of another, and then still others closer to the P-plane. Finally after continuing along this chain of connections one might come to a datum, one of the x's, on the P-plane, beyond the realm of one's own mental constructions. One would thus have reached the plane of experience and data, and connected the first concept and all the intervening ones with it and with one another.

Considering their origins and functions, concepts may be divided into two classes, those that lie relatively close to the P-plane and those much farther away. In the diagram the separation of these classes is symbolized by a no man's land between them in which relatively few circles appear. Those of the first kind derive their meaning much more directly from the experiential situation and their proximity to data; those of the second more immediately from theoretical considerations. The former come into being mainly as part of the scientific activity represented by circle *a* of Fig. 2,* and are the concepts that are typical of Table I and column A of Table V.† In these concepts the component of meaning-by-experience or -by-empirical analysis predominates. Some of them are anchored directly to the data (the x's) by double lines.‡ These represent observables and measurables such as distance, time interval, and mass in mechanics; angles and intensities in optics; pressure, volume and temperature in the physics of gases; and many more in these and other fields. Those to the left of no man's

* See diagram, p. 69.
† See pp. 144–145.
‡ These double lines represent what have variously been called *rules of correspondence, epistemic connections,* or *operational definitions.* Their role is very important, though we can not expound it adequately here.

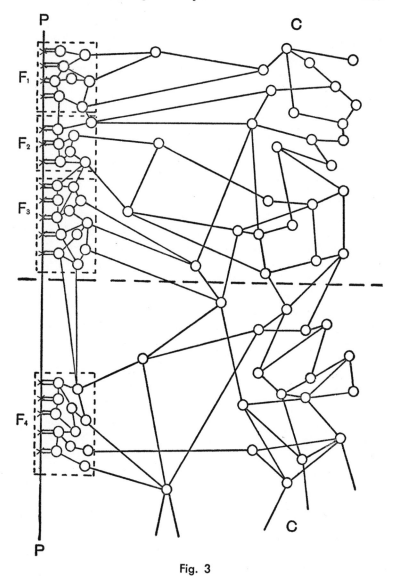

Fig. 3

Margenau Type Diagram Depicting Scientific Method

land include also such relational concepts as velocity, acceleration, momentum, index of refraction and focal distance, and phenomenological ones like reflection, refraction, interference, diffraction, and dispersion, electric charge, electric current, heat, temperature.

In Fig. 3 several groups of data and concepts closely related to them have been enclosed by dashed rectangles F_1, F_2, F_3, and so on. These combinations of data and concepts closely related to them represent *facts* according to my usage of the term.

The concepts to the right of the gap emerge in the main from the theoretical activity of circle *b* of Fig. 2, and are typical of Table II and column C in Table V. In these cases the component of meaning-by-postulation predominates. Here we meet the kinetic theory of gases with its mental constructs, such as molecules, kinetic agitation, random motion, change in momentum; optical theory with its constructs, such as waves and corpuscles, wave fronts and rays, Huyghens' Principle, destructive and constructive interference, electric and magnetic field vectors, and so on. Without at the moment trying to define a *theory* rigorously, we may characterize it as a structure of concepts (constructs), bound together by a coherent network of logical (and in some sciences mathematical) connections, and anchored to a particular body of data and facts.

Many theories are relatively independent structures, for instance the kinetic theory and the Maxwellian electromagnetic theory of light, and recognizably separate from the body of data and facts to which they are related. The facts also are relatively independent and recognizably separate. And yet neither theories nor facts are completely so, as is indicated in the figure by the circles in the gap and the connecting lines crossing it. Likewise no individual concept is either wholly theoretical or factual, postulational or experiential, but both in various degrees.

Let the upper part of Fig. 3 (above the horizontal dashed line) represent a particular theory with its epistemic connections to a body of data. What this diagram helps us to see then is that according to this conception, such a theory is not expected to provide a "picture" or mirror image of "unseen realities" beyond the P-plane of experience. It is initially simply a symbolic scheme wherewith to *explain* by means of various relationships among the facts of experience, e.g., how they are *causally* related, how data vary together in different ways, what magnitudes particular variables may be expected to have under certain specified conditions, and how phenomena and natural laws may be thought of in terms of certain postulated images and models.

Beyond that, however, if a theory is to be wholly acceptable it must do more than correlate and explain what is already known, it must also enlarge our experience by leading us to new, hitherto unobserved data and facts. It must predict under what circumstances these might be found. In other words, as we have said earlier, it must be conceptually fertile. If it is successful in this way, the ensemble of existing concepts will grow by the construction of new ones and will finally point to new data.

The way this works is illustrated in the figure. The theory which may have been confined, to begin with, to the area above the horizontal line by its preoccupation with a group of established facts, grows conceptually and is extended into the formerly unoccupied territory of the C-field (i.e., below the line), where it finally comes to point predictively toward hitherto unknown data and facts, and specify under what conditions, and where along the P-plane, they may be found. The process of verifying this prediction then consists of making observations and experiments under those conditions. If it is verified it can then be said that the theory has led from, say, the familiar facts F_1, F_2, and F_3 to the new ones F_4 and F_5.

This type of diagram helps us to understand that the validation of a theory, the process of actually touching down on the P-plane in the laboratory, means simply, as far as the theory itself is concerned, that its predictions have been found to be valid, that it is a truly useful tool, and that its fertility has enabled us to gain new knowledge. It does not mean that some sort of pictorial correspondence between the theory and nature has been demonstrated, or that it has been proved to be true and not false, for it is evident that a different conceptual network might possibly have been constructed to connect the same data, and to establish a path from the known and to the unknown. Indeed, a combination of other concepts, i.e., another theory, might have achieved the same results more easily, with fewer intermediate logical steps. In that case we would probably speak of a *simpler* theory, and would therefore regard it as superior to the first.

We may say therefore that while this validation has not established the truth of the theory, it has led to the discovery of truth, since it has confirmed the existence of facts not before known. Relating this scheme of science and its methods to what we have studied in earlier chapters, it seems clear that permanence, certainty and truth, as we have used these terms, reside to the left of the gap in the C-field, and that transience, adaptability, and conceptual fertility are on the right. With regard to the two streams in the history of science, the experiential-empirical one (Table V, column A) consists of the steady accumulation of the factual knowledge represented on the left side of Fig. 3. The other, the stream of theories (Table V, column C) consists of the constant modification or abandonment and replacement of the symbolic, conceptual networks on the right. The individual concepts closely associated with data and fact seem to remain essentially unchanged and in use permanently in history, while many of those on the right come and go in the flux and transience of the theoretical shifts.

This last remark prompts us to recall once more the axiom propounded by Professor Daniel Day Williams, that "all knowledge whatsoever is derived from a critical interpretation of what is given in human experience." For in the perspective provided by this concept-emphasizing point of view, reflection upon the methods of other fields seems to suggest compellingly that scientific method is indeed but an application of the general methods of intelligence, and is therefore *in essence* no different from the methods of all disciplines seeking knowledge. Certainly for all of them there are a P-plane, the gateway through which the "outside world" that is the object of inquiry impresses itself upon human consciousness, and a C-field of concepts. Surely to provide an interpretation always means to construct a structure of "critically" conceived ideas connected logically. And if it is to be an interpretation of something objective, that structure must be connected to the data of experience by which that something has made itself known to us. The Williams dictum is then equivalent to saying that the Margenau diagram is applicable to all fields in which knowledge is sought—including the field of religion.

2 · SHIFTS IN MEANINGS OF METHODOLOGICAL TERMS

We must recognize, however, that the meanings of certain methodological terms shift as we pass from one discipline to another. Sometimes the term *knowledge* is thought to have a narrowly restricted and fixed meaning that applies in all fields—*if* it applies at all. But surely this cannot be so, for both that which is known and the operations by which it becomes known change from object to object and field to field. To know that a sodium flame emits yellow light having specified wave lengths is very different, substantively and operationally, from knowing that water consists of oxygen and hydrogen, or that a star is a thousand light years distant, or that a given plant is alive or dead. And to know that Abraham Lincoln lived, that Beethoven's violin concerto is beautiful, and that God is Love is something else again. This variety of knowledge-claims, all of which stem basically from experience and critical thinking, suggests that there is in actual usage a gradual shift in the meaning of the term *knowledge*. While the propriety of using the word *knowledge* in some of these cases is denied by some, it seems advantageous nevertheless to allow the term *knowledge* for all of them, thus emphasizing that in an important sense they are basically alike, while at the same time admitting a shift in its specific meaning from field to field. At this point an analogy may be helpful, namely that of a continuous optical spectrum. I suggest that the various meanings of *knowledge* are as different as the infra-red, red, green, violet and ultraviolet bands of a continuous spectrum of electromagnetic radiation, and yet are as basically alike in nature as these are. While the techniques of observing and conceptualizing ultra-violet light are in many respects very different from those we must use when dealing with infra-red or with "visible" light, this does not mean that these different bands of the spectrum cannot be regarded as basically the same in essence. Certainly they all have wave length and frequency, though these change from band to band. In material media they propagate at different velocities, are absorbed at different rates, have different chemical effects. Nevertheless they are all "light"—in a sense the same light.

3 · THE CONTINUOUS SPECTRUM OF COGNITION

This leads me to propose that the analogy of the continuous spectra applies to cognition in general, that is to virtually all the key terms used in this chapter, namely perception, P-plane, experience, C-field, concepts, interconcept connections, rules of correspondence, epistemic connections, operational definitions, data, objects, theories, prediction, verification, validation, truth, conceptual fertility, explanation, and perhaps still others. The totality of meaning of each of these may, I submit, be represented by a continuous spectrum covering all fields of knowledge, from the physical to the biological and social sciences, the arts, and religion. This means that if Fig. 3 as it stands is taken to represent, say, physics, and we extend downward the line symbolizing the P-plane, and with it the C-field, to take in successively the fields of chemistry, geology, biology, psychology, anthropology, sociology, political science, the arts and religion-theology, along with other fields properly placed among these, we shall be laying out such a continuous spectrum—of experience and perception, and of concepts and interpretations.

What this wide sweep of *experience, concepts* and *theory* means I have explained in preceding chapters. Moreover, I have shown in some detail how these three terms differ in kind at opposite ends of this spectrum, i.e., in science (especially physics) and in religion respectively. Therefore there is no need to expound them further, except to remark briefly on the continuity of meaning of one term: *perception*. This is usually taken to have a rather narrow meaning, namely the process by which data of experience become available to us *through the senses and their instrumental extensions*. This restriction seems to be neither necessary nor desirable. It is a fact of life that men do become aware of realities outside themselves by processes that we do not understand, but that certainly transcend perception by the senses alone. Certainly men do claim somehow to perceive beauty, goodness, justice, holiness, the presence of God. Man is so constituted that many kinds of realities that are external to him can impress themselves coercively upon him. This becoming aware of something given in experience —whatever it may be—I call perception.

With these meanings in mind, let us look at some other variables in the cognitive spectrum. At its upper end, in the physical sciences, data are sense data that are in large part quantitative and measurable. Moreover their nature is such that it is relatively easy for different observers to agree on them, and thus to verify one another's experimental findings. The concepts and theories also tend to be quantitative and therefore mathematically expressible. Furthermore, the theories are typically bound so tightly to the basic data, that they can be validated without too much disagreement. No doubt this is one reason why at any one time the number of competing theories is usually very small, rarely more than two. All this is true even though in contemporary physics and chemistry the phenomena studied are often very far removed from everyday life and immediate perception, and that concepts and theories are highly sophisticated and symbolic.

As we pass downward along the spectrum, through the biological and social sciences and beyond, all this changes gradually and eventually becomes significantly different. Less and less are the data simply sense percepts. More and more difficult does it become to handle them quantitatively, and to conceive of them precisely. Theories become progressively less mathematical. Interpersonal communication and cross-checks and therefore verification become less easy. More and more, people disagree about the data and facts, as well as the validity of theories. Competing theories and interpretations become more numerous. The gap in the C-field between theories and facts becomes narrower. All this is very evident even within science itself, where the differences between the physical and social sciences are in these respects quite pronounced. No wonder they seem even more glaringly evident in the arts and in religion. And yet, withal, basically the insights and knowledge in all of them are gained by methods that are in essence the same. The Margenau diagram *is* applicable to them all. Knowledge is *one*. In all fields it is gained by the interplay of given data and constructed concepts—though these may display different properties in different fields.

One final remark about the spectrum. The analogy envisages a *continuous* spectrum, because it is without discontinuities or gaps, and without boundary lines separating its various sections. There is only one continuum of experience, only one P-plane and one C-field extending unbroken throughout the entire length of the spectrum—the entire realm of knowledge. No one can say where physics ends and chemistry begins. Nor is there a dividing line between biology and psychology. And this continuity extends into the realm of religion as well.

4 · INTER-DISCIPLINARY APPROPRIATION OF CONCEPTS

Not only is there this continuity along the spectrum, but there is within it an immense amount of interdiffusion and interaction among the concepts of the various disciplines. Thus many ideas and theories of physics are integrally connected with those of chemistry and biology, in the sense that they have been adopted and adapted by them. These are in turn connected with those of the social sciences, and so on. Moreover, their data also seem to be related in various ways, both experientially and conceptually.

Nor is this interdiffusion and interaction apparent only in what might be called the borderlands created by the inevitable overlapping of neighboring fields, such as physics and chemistry, or botany and zoology, but it may occur between widely separated ones, such as physics and psychology or even sociology and politics. Nor is this effect unknown in the relations between physics and theology, which may be thought of as separated by virtually the entire length of the spectrum. For good or for ill, the fact is that conceptions of physics have affected concepts of religious thought and theology to a considerable extent, as we have seen earlier. Though it may be surprising, there has been at times a reverse interaction. A notorious historical case in point is the origin of the important physical *principle of least action,* which seems to have been proposed by Maupertuis on theological grounds.[3] I am not at the moment saying that this sort of thing is desirable—or undesirable, for that matter—but rather simply reporting that it has occurred.

That these inter-disciplinary appropriations of concepts do occur should not be too surprising, since after all the human mind and consciousness are so constituted that there exists only one continuum or field of concepts. A given concept that may be already at hand and is therefore available for whatever purpose it may serve, may consequently be commandeered for use in different theoretical structures. Since there are no confining partitions in the mind, or the C-field, there is nothing to prevent the appropriation of any given concept by different disciplines. This is not in itself undesirable. It becomes undesirable only when the insertion of a concept, from wherever it may have come, invalidates a theory, i.e., when its correlating and predicting functions are thereby impaired, or when its simplicity and elegance or other such desirable qualities are thereby damaged or lost.

If a concept from physics contributes to the success of a chemical or biological theory, well and good. By the same token, if a scientific concept contributes to the success of a philosophical or theological theory—or vice versa—well and good. There is no prohibition in either scientific or theological methodology against such appropriation of foreign concepts—*if* it serves proper purposes and actually achieves desirable ends.

For a long time in the history of science it was customary for scientists to plug gaps or holes in their theories by inserting theological conceptions into them. It is well known that Newton did just that, when in what purported to be a scientific explanation of the eye he inserted the God concept to complete the explanation. He did likewise when he felt his theory of gravitation to be inadequate for the complete explanation of planetary motion.[4] The case of Newton was not, of course, an isolated one.

In terms of the criteria of acceptability of theories prevailing then, such practices seemed quite appropriate. Today they no longer do. The criteria have changed. Our present-day conceptions of the purpose of science, and of the way that purpose can be realized, has led to conceptions of theory that make such hole-plugging processes thoroughly unacceptable. We now realize that there are both practical and logical reasons for thinking that the insertion of the concept of God into a scientific theory cannot contribute to the solution of any *scientific* problem. It does not help us to provide a *scientific* explanation of any phenomenon, or to predict the occurrence of any natural event. This is, no doubt, the fundamental reason why physical scientists resist any suggestion that religious categories be incorporated in their theories.

There seems to be a tendency today in certain quarters to introduce physical concepts into theological theorizing, in the attempt to do some hole-plugging in reverse. It seems to me that much of the talk about the alleged theological implications of the celebrated Uncertainty Principle comes under this heading. No doubt one potent reason why most theologians seem to resist this sort of thing is that they regard it as fruitless. According to contemporary conceptions of the purpose of theology and theological theory, it does not contribute to the solution of any *theological or religious* problem or provide a *religiously* adequate explanation of any religious phenomenon. There are both practical and logical reasons for supposing that the *religious* usefulness and fertility of theological theory are impaired thereby.

Another tendency in the same direction, though of a rather different kind, is that of seeking to substitute scientific concepts for existing religious ones in attempts to develop a "new religion," a "scientific religion" or a "religion of science." A case in point is the substitution of the concept of evolution for the concept of God in seeking to construct a new doctrine of ultimate purpose and destiny. The reason why many theologians resist this is, no doubt, basically the same as the reason why scientists would resist attempts to construct a "new science," a "religious science" or a "science of religion," and to solve scientific problems by substituting religious concepts and doctrines for scientific ones. They can see no way by which truly religious problems can be solved in terms of scientific concepts. Whether such doubts and fears are justifiable or not only the future can tell. I can see no way of deciding the matter in principle. It just might turn out that certain important concepts can be seen to have both scientific and religious meaning, and that thereby scientific and religious doctrines may be brought together in a truly significant way.

5 · OTHER EXTERNAL INFLUENCES

Thus far we have considered how a given field may be influenced from the outside through the infiltration or adoption of concepts from other fields. In this way the conceptual content of theories may be affected and thus strengthened or weakened, or even invalidated. There are, of course, other kinds of external pressures that have serious consequences. One is the intrusion of points of view and values that are not, strictly speaking, native in origin or purpose. Along these lines historical studies during recent decades have shown rather conclusively that in fact the acceptance or rejection of scientific theories has often been affected or even determined largely by philosophical, economic, technological, political and religious considerations. Especially is this true of theories of great generality, since there seems to be an almost irresistible tendency to extend their meaning beyond their technical import, into realms of wider significance, and to apply them to non-scientific questions. No sooner did Copernicus construct a conception of the solar system that made the sun a centrally fixed body and placed the earth among the moving planets, than it was charged that the reliability of Holy Writ and the validity of Aristotelian philosophy were being undermined. Thus there were ascribed to this revolutionary physical perspective momentous non-physical implications for life in general, and this led to its being subjected to non-scientific critique and evaluation. No sooner was all matter conceived for particular purposes as consisting of tiny particles rigorously "obeying" the Newtonian laws of motion, than the world was for general purposes thought of as entirely determinate, thus obviating the need for the religious conception of divine providence, and, indeed, of divinity itself. This conception had then to be evaluated not only for its technical meaning in science, but for its even more important significance elsewhere. Once the idea of physical laws or natural laws took hold, these were soon interpreted by analogy to be ethical laws also. With the advent of uncertainty and probability concepts in theoretical physics, the freedom of the will is now supposed by some to have been reestablished in the economy of things—and therefore the quantum theory must now run the gantlet not only of scientific but of philosophical and theological battering. Moreover, once a scientific theory has gained general acceptance on these various grounds it takes on the status in the public mind of an a-priori axiom, and it becomes exceedingly difficult to discard it for scientific reasons only, i.e., when from the viewpoint of science itself it should be abandoned in favor of another. It is then demanded that other objectives and values be taken into account also.

It must not be supposed that these non-scientific reasons for accepting or rejecting scientific theories have operated only outside of the science community and in the dim past. After all, scientists are human beings with deep concerns. Virtually all of them realize that life cannot be lived divided into separate compartments, and that what they do and think must fit into the totality of things and have meaning relative to the common good. Inevitably these concerns make themselves felt in their work. In these respects present-day scientists are probably not fundamentally different from their forebears.

Perhaps no example is more instructive in regard to what goes on today than that presented by the Russian community of science, whose basic rationale of science and its method includes doctrines derived from Marxist philosophy and a sense of responsibility to the State. And such views, competent observers assure us, are no longer merely imposed by authority, but have to a considerable extent become indigenous to scientific thought itself. Whether such views are misguided or not is for present purposes irrelevant. The point is that there is a large competent contemporary community of scientists who in the evaluation and acceptance of scientific theories give high priority to what we of the non-communist world would regard as non-scientific reasons.[5]

With reference to the question of the past versus the present, it cannot be denied, of course, that certain points of view concerning scientific methodology once held by scientists are no longer acceptable today. Science does change its mind, not only about what is acceptable in the content of its thought but in its ideals and the methods it employs. The contemporary ideal of "hands off," that calls for keeping intrusions and infiltrations to a minimum and for eliminating them if possible, represents a tremendous advance. So does the present view that theories shall be judged by their fertility instead of an alleged correspondence with nature. But progress in these directions does not signify that scientists are less human than their forebears, less a part of the real world, or less concerned

about the ultimate significance and consequences of their enterprise and its intellectual and technological products.

That religion and religious thought are also subject to external
influences, and that the latter are very potent, has been recognized
for a long time. Indeed the dangers inherent in the infiltration and
adoption of ideas and attitudes "foreign" to any given religion
have been the subject of perennial warnings by its prophets. Like
those of science, these intrusions are numerous and varied, and include economic, philosophical, scientific, political, sociological
and even competing religious points of view and pressures. Moreover, these pressures appear at the same points—in addition to
others. Thus criteria for the acceptance of religious doctrines have
by no means been exclusively religious. Practical considerations,
often well intended but misguided, have intruded. Totalitarian
philosophies have often sought to take control. Moreover to religious and theological teachings there have often been ascribed
universal significance and authority that from a purely religious
point of view were never intended, and that consequently subjected them to philosophical, scientific and political scrutiny,
criticism and attack.

Religion is, of course, much more vulnerable to such external
influences than is science, because of its very nature. For one thing,
it is by intent and purpose an involvement in, and a deep concern
for, life in all its aspects. In a demanding sense it must not live
for itself or by itself. Indeed in a still deeper sense religion is not
something in itself, but something that seeks to permeate and be
inseparable from life wherever it is lived. Inevitably then it must
touch, say, economics and politics in a way that science never can.

In religion there is therefore a perpetual tension: to be in the
world, but not of it; to influence it, but not be sullied by it. It *must*
identify itself with the world, and yet *must not* identify with it.
Under these conditions and with these purposes, it is inevitable
that the interaction between religious communities and their environment is much more intimate and consequential, and much
more dangerous and stimulating, than is the interaction between
the science community and its surroundings.

6 · DEPENDENCE ON SOCIETY

Not only are the communities of science and religion *influenced* by their surroundings, but they are *dependent* on them, not only, say, economically, requiring institutional and material support, but intellectually. They are not self-sustaining or self-sufficient, as if they were isolated and independent of their culture. For one thing, they are indebted to society for its general, as distinguished from their own special, instruments of thought such as language and logic. For another, they are beholden to society for characteristic ways of thinking, and for subtle feelings that have come out of cultural experience, and have helped to shape them in significant ways.

Thinking now of science especially, I refer to the kind of factors that must have operated in the Occident to produce "western science" as we know it, rather than the very different kind of science that has been native to the Orient, say to China.[6] I mean those factors that are essentially nonscientific in nature and yet bring about crises, turning points and revolutions in the history of ideas and of science. The following sentences from the pen of Herbert Butterfield, renowned British historian, seem apropos here:

> It is never easy—if it is possible at all—to feel that one has reached the bottom of a matter, or touched the last limit of explanation, when dealing with an historical transition. It would appear that the most fundamental changes in outlook, the most remarkable turns in the current of intellectual fashion, may be referable in the last resort to an alteration in men's feelings for things, an alteration at once so subtle and so generally pervasive that it cannot be attributed to any particular writers or any influence of academic thought as such. . . . Subtle changes like this—the result not of any book but of the new texture of human experience in a new age—are apparent behind the story of the scientific revolution.[7]

In this connection he refers to changes in "men's feelings for matter itself," in the "habitual use of words" and an increasing interest in "the operation of pure mechanism." Elsewhere he points to others.

Perhaps one should mention also Whitehead's thesis, that among the factors that have created a favorable climate for the growth of science in the West was Christianity, with its "habit of definite exact thought . . . implanted in the European mind by the long dominance of scholastic logic and scholastic divinity," its "inexpugnable belief that every detailed occurrence can be correlated with its antecedents in a perfectly definite manner"—which belief came "from the medieval insistence on the rationality of God." Whitehead did not refer to the "explicit beliefs of a few individuals" but to the "impress on the European mind arising from the unquestioned faith of centuries," to "the instinctive tone of thought and not a mere creed of words." [8]

As far as religious thought is concerned, there is the same sort of dependence upon cultural factors. No doubt the subtle changes in the feelings of men regarding matter, and the changes in the way words are used, are operative here too. Certainly it is common knowledge that the imagery of early Christian thought was shaped to a large extent by the cosmological conceptions of the time, that this imagery became a part of the very fabric of Christian theology and that a traumatic wrenching of thought ensued when many centuries later that cosmology was replaced by another. It is well known too that Christian theology depended upon Aristotelian philosophy, aside from cosmology, for a long period of church history. In more recent times the triumph of evolution was responsible to a large extent for the appearance of what has come to be called the "theology of the liberal era." Then the disillusionment resulting from the First World War provided a setting for the rise of so called "crisis theology." All this is so well known that we need not go into further details here.

There is one aspect of the dependence of religion upon environment that needs our attention, especially because it may be a rather serious matter today. In Chapter II it was pointed out that religion differs from science in that it is concerned with ultimacy and depth, and that to express these concerns and to talk about God it needs symbolic language. But if these symbols are to be truly meaningful they must be symbols that are in use elsewhere, i.e., have meaning in their own right in the culture of the time. Now it seems that there have been times in history when no adequate symbols were available and when it therefore became virtually impossible to theologize. Professor John Dillenberger calls attention to this phenomenon in referring to the impact of Darwinism upon theology.

> The Darwinian impact was the final threat to all the vertical and depth dimension within man and the cosmos. It marked the culmination of a period in which no adequate symbols were left for expressing and thinking about the classical Christian heritage. . . . The late nineteenth and early twentieth centuries may have been one of those rare periods in history in which theology was virtually impossible, when the crisis of language and imagination excluded the essential depth of both God and man.

Later he observes:

> The history of science *does* mean that the old ways of putting things are no longer viable. It *does not* mean that the essential content of theology is thereby changed.

But he says still later:

> In the history of the Western world, the old pictures and symbols have disappeared. . . . In our contemporary world, new symbols and analogies may well arise, and many of them may again be more adequate than those in the more recent past.[9]

The nature of theology is such then that it is dependent upon culture to provide it with adequate linguistic and conceptual symbols for the expression of its insights. It cannot create new terms for its own use as freely as science can, for as far as possible it must use the language of the people. Symbols expressing ultimate concern, that are adequate for worship and prayer and for instruction in things divine, are not constructed at will and at short notice, but grow out of the life and thought of people gradually and slowly. Theology is largely meaningless today, to many people both inside and outside of the Church, because for the most part it uses symbols that were once meaningful but are so no longer to any large extent. Not only does this tell us much about the nature of religion, but about its dependence upon the culture.

Returning to science, the last, but by no means least important, non-scientific support of science provided by its environment is its ethics, as expressed by the following few commandments: Thou shalt not steal another scientist's ideas or data. If thou wishest to borrow or adopt and adapt them, thou shalt give proper credit for them. Thou shalt report thine own data honestly and not make false claims. It has been suggested that these principles of professional ethics have come spontaneously out of the work and thought of the science community, more specifically out of the necessities of self preservation. If men were not scrupulously honest in reporting their findings, so the argument goes, others could not build on them. There could not then be progress, and thus science would die. False data lead men into blind alleys, and result in waste. This sort of explanation constitutes a kind of hypothesis of the survival of the honest, and a perishing of the dishonest. It no doubt would be much more difficult to substantiate this than an assertion that these ethical principles of science are a gift of its cultural environment.

7 · "PRESUPPOSITIONS"

An important aspect of any field of study is its preconceptual foundation, the basic axioms or postulates upon which it is said to rest, without which conceivably it could not exist. This is often referred to in short as its *presuppositions*. The term is misleading. For one thing, it seems to convey so many different meanings that only rarely can one be sure just what is intended in any particular context. Moreover, it seems to have certain implications or overtones of a deliberate, conscious, systematic "making up one's mind in advance" that gives the wrong impression as to the facts in the case of science. Therefore I prefer more definite terms such as predispositions, preunderstandings, preconceptions, instinctive beliefs and postulates. Let us look at some of these with special reference now to science and later to religion.[10]

One of the standard meanings of the word *presupposition* refers to what I shall call *common understandings* that underlie all quests for knowledge—scientific, humanistic and religious. A few of these that certainly constitute a part of the foundation of science may be formulated as follows: You and I, others like us, and the world about us, exist. We can achieve some understanding of the world and of one another. This understanding can be communicated. Assertions made in communicating may be meaningful in various ways, e.g., with reference to experienced truth, theoretical validity, logical self-consistency and so on.

Science is said to rest also on a second kind of presuppositional foundation, namely on certain predilections, capacities and values that seem to be distinctively human. Among these are intellectual curiosity and the urge to explore the unknown; imagination and the tendency to create abstract worlds; the drive to analyze, be self-critical, to take apart; the desire to explain; the ability and disposition to symbolize, quantify, measure, compute and experiment. In this connection one finds references also to certain indispensable social values such as freedom, tolerance, mutual confidence, active cooperation, intellectual honesty. That there could be no science without these seems to be indubitable. Again it must be said, however, that science is not unique in this respect, for most of them are prerequisites also to the existence and success of the arts, as well as religion.

Thinking now more especially about the natural sciences, one finds in the literature certain preunderstandings that do have special meaning for them (third type). They are the ones that pertain specifically to *nature,* and assume that it is real, orderly and in principle predictable, describable in terms of quantitative relations, and basically, as far as its fundamental laws are concerned, unchanging in time and uniform throughout space.

There is something curious about all these and other such presuppositions. So far as I am aware no one doubts that in some sense they constitute the foundation upon which science rests. And yet science itself pays virtually no attention to them. One does not usually find them listed or discussed in scientific treatises. They are not taught to science students, elementary or advanced, as part of the science curriculum. Most scientists regard them as belonging to philosophy rather than science.

This says something very interesting and significant about science, at least about natural science. It is not the kind of intellectual enterprise that requires its participants to lay a logical foundation for their work before they can proceed with it. It simply says, Come, let us do physics, or chemistry, or geology. Let us open our eyes and look around. Let us try to find out how things work, how they hang together, how things follow upon one another. Let us give names, i.e., concepts, to what we see and to the relations we discern in what we observe. Let us also measure, experiment, theorize and use what we learn for the transformative betterment of the world and of life. If one accepts this invitation or summons, one soon finds oneself immersed in the work, and as far as the needs of that work are concerned the question almost never arises as to whether it makes sense logically, or what there is about the universe and its economy that makes its doing possible, or why it is that it is not impossible.

Clearly, then, these fundamental understandings are not existentially of the nature of deliberate presupposings or carefully formulated postulates. Nor are they in any sense intrusions into science from a different, alien world. Rather they represent, at least in part, an elemental, unconscious or subconscious participation in the intuitive, instinctive understandings of the contemporary culture. They come out of its common ways of taking for granted, reacting to and believing in nature. In part also, as far as a particular scientist and generation of scientists are concerned, they are accepted at first informally as implicit, unstructured elements of a common heritage from the past. In both these aspects they are expressions of a pervasive *Zeitgeist,* which science helps to shape but by which it is itself molded.

It is, of course, a fact that these informal cultural preunderstandings have found formal expression. One does find them discussed explicitly.[11] From the viewpoint of a restricted conception of science, the business of smoking out these hidden preconceptions, of analyzing them critically and finally giving them the status of basic postulates, is not part of the work of science itself, but of philosophy. On the other hand, increasingly the science community is interesting itself in such matters and is taking the position that the study of the philosophy and history of science is a part of its own business and is therefore part of science itself.* From this point of view, however, such presuppositions as we have men-

---

* It has been said repeatedly that perhaps only a physicist knows enough about physics itself, i.e., intimately from the inside, to construct a theory or philosophy of the nature and method of physics that is anchored in the actualities of the enterprise of physics, and that the professional philosopher is more likely to construct a philosophy of physics as he thinks it ought to be, or as he constructs it abstractly. We probably need both points of view.

tioned have a dual aspect, and should be recognized as developing in two stages or phases. As I have said, in the lives of individuals and of generations of scientists they are at first subconscious pre-understandings. This might be called the pre-phase. Only later, in a post-phase, do they become formalized. This happens, apparently, as the result of critical thinking necessitated by new communal experience as each new generation comes along. Thus one can say that these presuppositions are at once the inherited foundation upon which science is built and the end product of science's critical thinking about itself. Each generation enriches and changes the meaning of these presuppositions through the contributions of its own work, and the implication of that work relative to the foundations of science. Thus the Copernican generation gave new meaning and content to the common understandings it inherited, and passed these on. In some generations the process of critical analysis and formal postulation receives more attention than others. Newton's generation, especially through Newton's own formulation of the *Principia,* was an outstanding contributor in this respect. Einstein's was likewise. In each case unusual interest and activity in the study of the foundations of science have been caused by great discoveries that called for new points of view and the re-examination of old ones.

So we find again that science is circular, from foundations to superstructure to foundations. From common understandings to technical knowledge to common understandings. From culture to science to culture. Perhaps the metaphor of a spiral is better than that of the circle. True, science goes around and around, but its history seems to show also a steady rise, each circle or loop being in general higher than its predecessor.

Now let us turn to religion. It seems to me that the situation there is surprisingly like that in science. Thus both have presuppositions of the first three classes. Looking at these in turn, those of the first, referring to common knowledge, appear to be essentially the same for both. Certainly religious thought—at least that of the Judaeo-Christian tradition—also assumes (the first kind) the existence of communicating selves; the reality of entities independent of minds; the possibility of truth, validity and meaningfulness. Likewise it is dependent upon (second kind) such elemental human qualities as curiosity, imagination, cooperation, trust, freedom and honesty. Furthermore, religious thought could not exist, any more than could science, without the primal urges of men to reason, symbolize, conceptualize, generalize and systematize.

As for the third type, those that are more especially significant for science, those referring to nature and its orderliness, predictability and quantitative explicability, these too are part of the body of common understandings that contemporary religious thought shares with scientific thought. The fact that such specific abilities and predilections as measurement and experimentation, and such particular assumptions as the invariance of natural laws in time and space, are not relevant to religion directly, does not invalidate the thesis that the foundations of religion and science are identical to a large extent. This is to be expected because both communities today come by these common understandings in the same way, in part instinctively through their own contact with nature and man, and in part through cultural inheritance.

Since, however, the realm explored by religious thought has also the dimension of depth and ultimacy, and religious experience includes awareness of the holy and faith in God, religion does have preunderstandings over and above those it shares with science. The following are a few examples: There exists a realm of ultimacy, mystery, and the holy. This is characterized by order and to some extent predictability. It can be understood at least in part. God is one. He reveals Himself and His will. Surely these correspond to those of the third kind that belong more uniquely to science. Moreover, religion is based in part on certain human abilities and urges not relevant directly to science, e.g., the urge to worship and pray.

Like those of science the preunderstandings of religion have a pre- and a post-phase. Initially they are informal, held unconsciously or subconsciously rather than explicitly. Later, as a result of living and critical thinking they come to the surface and seek attention and formulation. In one sense they are foundation, and in another superstructure. They are circular in their relation to religious experience and thought. The nature of religion, certainly Christianity, is such that presuppositions of this sort do not seem important to begin with. Christianity does not, any more than science, demand that novitiates think first about basic presuppositions, satisfy themselves that there is a realm of the spirit, that it is orderly and dependable, that it makes logical sense to entertain ultimate concerns, to believe in God and man, and to love both. It says: Come join us in faith, in doing the will of God, in accepting His grace and forgiveness. There is work to be done in the world in the name of God. There is a Gospel to proclaim, truth to be communicated.

If the novice accepts this invitation or summons he will find himself immersed in faith and work. Questions as to the rationale of the possibility and validity of his life and relationship to God may not arise for a long time. This is the pre-phase of his relation to these basic understandings. Later, for various reasons, there will come times of critical evaluation and analysis. This will be the post-phase that leads to explicit formulations of presuppositions.

Depending, however, on the time in history when he and his contemporaries live and when this maturing process from pre- to post-supposings takes place, the post-product of a generation's lifetime may represent either an enrichment or an impoverishment of the fundamental common understandings. It seems clear that in the long run these have developed upward toward richer insight from one era to another, as we saw in Chapter IX in connection with Table VI. Thus there *is* a progressive revelation disclosing more and more facets of the love of God. But sometimes in the shorter run, say within the life-span of a few generations, there may be impoverishment—as when the store of symbols available for expressing religious insight becomes vanishingly small. This is the kind of situation identified by Dillenberger in connection with the impact of Darwinism. Occasionally, however, an even more devastating situation develops. Thus not long after the Newtonian synthesis had been achieved, certainly by the time Laplace came along, who gave expression to a completely deterministic conception of the universe, not only were the common understandings practically bare of any symbols in terms of which to think about God, but it seemed almost meaningless to think about God at all. The purposes and processes that had been assigned to God, so to speak, seemed taken care of in other ways. There was no need for Him any more. The universe was thought of as self-sustaining. The basic difficulty was—so it seems now by hindsight—that the God concept and common understanding had come to be anchored not in religion itself so much as in cosmology and metaphysics.

8 · DISTINCTIVELY COMMUNAL PRECONCEPTIONS

Lucien Price [12] reports Whitehead as saying repeatedly that all of the basic assumptions of science he learned as a student at Cambridge were set aside during his lifetime. What he was talking about, apparently, was another (fourth) kind of presupposition, one that was a more distinctively scientific preconception—one that came, for the most part, largely from science itself rather than from common experience and common understanding. Here are some examples: Space is Euclidian. There is an aether filling space. The total amounts of matter and of energy respectively in the universe are each constant in time. Matter is discontinuous, made up of particles that are eternal and immutable. Radiation is continuous, made up of electromagnetic waves. The motions of the fundamental particles are governed by the Newtonian laws of motion.

Here we encounter for the first time in our discussion a kind of truly scientific fundamental assumption upon which logical developments are actually based formally and which are consciously and inextricably entwined with all aspects of the everyday work and conscious thought of the scientist. These are the formally postulated ideas on which others are built, and that are more than feelings and attitudes and instinctive taking things for granted. These are the ones that are native to science itself, are expounded explicitly in the scientific treatises, and are indispensable to adequate exposition. Without them we could have no science, conceived as a tough-minded, rigorous, and intellectual discipline. Clearly these are what we have earlier called the creeds or dogmas of science.

In religion obviously the analog of this fourth kind of presupposition is the religious creed, the kind of I-believe statement that is basic explicitly to religious thought and refers to the nature and structure of spiritual or divine reality. These are the assumptions upon which the theoretical structures of theology are founded. Without them we could have no theology, conceived now also as a tough-minded, rigorous and intellectual discipline.

These scientific and religious creeds also have both an implicit, informal pre-aspect and an explicit, propositional post-phase; an experiential and intuitive faith phase, and an interpretive theory phase. Eventually deep experience and faith achieve articulate expression, theoretical "explanation," and doctrinal formulation. Thus arise the post-phases and -functions of religious creeds, and this is why in time they become sophisticated and replete with abstractions.

Consider, for example, the scientific creedal presupposition about cause and effect. As commonly understood, it represents implicit ideas corresponding closely to immediate experience. As such it expresses, in common-sense language, an elemental faith in the dependability of nature, and a belief that successive events hang together and are not chaotically independent. Thus regarded it is a scientific creed-by-intuition. With the historical growth of scientific experience and thought, and in response to the need for articulation and interpretation, this simple creed has gradually been transformed by the emergence of highly sophisticated meanings far removed from those of ordinary usage. What is technically called the "causality principle" in modern physics certainly says much more than the common-sense view of cause and effect would imply. Its full explication requires reference to a large variety of concepts, such as efficacy, uniformity, identity, contiguity, simultaneity and succession; dynamical and statistical causality; absolute necessity and probability of connection. Moreover, it requires us to distinguish carefully between the world of conceptual structures and that of common experience, between propositions about cognitions and those concerning things and events. Here in its explicit post-phase, we have a scientific creed-by-postulation.

Again I must repudiate any impression that the intuitive and postulational aspects of presuppositions and assumptions can be distinguished or differentiated sharply, or that in the experience of individual and community they operate independently, and are necessarily separated temporally. While, as I see it, there can be no doubt that they may be separated at times, it is equally true that sometimes they are not. Perhaps they are never actually completely apart.

9 · NEGATIVE PRESUPPOSITIONS

It is apparent that what science is interested in fundamentally is what actually happens in nature—not what does not or cannot happen. The relationships it endeavors to discover are positive ones. Its knowledge is couched predominantly in the language of positive assertions, not denials. Its laws and principles deal with the known, not the unknown; with the probable, not the impossible. Very few of them are stated as negative conclusions. And yet some of the most profound effects of science in the realm of common understanding have been negative in nature. Witness its influence in the direction of the reduction of superstition and the elimination of magic—through the denial of falsehood quite as much as the affirmation of truth. And so it has come about that many common understandings that have resulted from science are negative. Therefore there are many presuppositions that have seeped out of science into the pool of common understanding and back again into science, that are commonly stated as denials. The following are a few examples that are part of our contemporary common understanding: There is no reality aside from physically observable reality. There is no realm of the supernatural. Minds cannot themselves affect physical events or phenomena causally. Extrasensory perception is impossible. There can be no foreknowledge of the future.[13]

Perhaps the first thing to notice about negative preunderstandings is that in the history of science there have been many that were once considered evident and yet later turned out to be false. Here are a few examples: An object cannot remain in motion unless a motor force acts upon it. Light cannot go around a corner. A chemical element is not transmutable into another. The mass of a body does not change if the amount of its matter does not change by chemical reaction or otherwise. Artificial parthenogenesis is impossible. Psychosomatic effects are impossible.

The second observation is that the nature of science and its processes are such that it is very much more difficult, if not impossible, to establish or verify a negative claim. One cannot observe, measure, or experiment with what does not or cannot happen. One cannot empirically verify negative claims—except indirectly. Thus one cannot say that electricity *cannot* show up in quantities less than the charge on the electron. One can only say that no such smaller charges have been observed and that the assumption that the electronic charge is the smallest that occurs in nature is a fertile one that fits in well with the prevailing theoretical idea of physics. One cannot logically say that heat *cannot* flow "up hill," i.e., from a body of low temperature to one of higher temperature, unaided. One can only say that it has not been observed to happen, and that the second law of thermodynamics that expresses this restriction is consistent with both experience and prevailing theory. Therefore whenever scientists become dogmatic with regard to these negative understandings they are on shaky ground, and are in danger of violating the ideals of science.

These remarks apply to religion-theology also. There too there have been negative presuppositions. One of them was that celestial bodies cannot have the same nature as terrestrial ones. This seems not to have been a formal, discrete doctrine so much as a general a-priori assumption. It played an important role in the disputes over the Copernican-Galilean astronomy and physics. Another was that there could be no fundamental change or transformation of the biological species. This was not apparently a specific, positive belief that came out of the Christian faith so much as a general assumption that seemed self-evident from certain common notions as to the nature of God and His creation. What God made was good enough and could not of itself change into something better or more advanced. This negative presupposition and others similar to it constituted troublesome issues in the controversies about evolution. A third negative assumption was that the Bible could not contain scientific errors. Since it was God's Word how could it? Here are a few examples of a different kind: Man cannot achieve "salvation" by his own efforts. Man cannot find God by pure reason. Science cannot provide answers to questions of ultimate concern. Science cannot describe or explain man in the entirety of his nature.

Clearly some of these negatives are legitimate offsprings of the Christian faith and others are not. Some became influential as common understandings and others did not. Some have come and gone. Others are still current today. Many of the difficulties between science and theology, past and present, have arisen from negative assumptions. When religion and science respectively have been dogmatic or authoritarian in their teachings and their proscription of opposing views—and both have been guilty in this respect—this has shown up almost always as clashes of denials rather than affirmations. Their warfare has not been so much over what they could legitimately claim in their own fields as what they have undertaken to deny in the field of the other. Both should recognize the essential indefensibility of most doctrinal denials, or of negative preconceptions, since by nature negative claims are in general not verifiable.

10 · THE GENERAL IMPLICATION

The Margenau type diagram may give the impression that a given scientific concept (construct) is related or connected in only two ways, on the one hand to data, and on the other to other scientific concepts in the C-field. Thus it may seem to emerge exclusively from purely scientific considerations in a deliberate, conscious effort of the scientist to construct a concept with only two meanings, one relative to the facts he is dealing with and the other to the theory he is trying to construct. If, however, the analysis of the chapter is correct, concepts and theories should be recognized as being rooted in part also in the common understandings of the cultural environment.

Many concepts have therefore a third relation and component of meaning: that designated earlier as meaning-by-presupposition (Table V, column B). In preceding chapters the role of intuition in conceptualization and apprehension has been emphasized as an important facet of presuppositional awareness that contributes to cognition. Also we pointed out the intimate, circular relationship that exists between intuition and the body of common and communal understandings. We even spoke there of meaning-by-inheritance. Thus the symbol "light B" was said to refer not only to the intuitive awareness of the presence or existence of light, but also to the unstructured communal or cultural belief that there is such a thing as light. This chapter may then be regarded as a more complete exposition of the origin, richness and complexity of meanings-by-presupposition, or -by-intuition, or -by-inheritance. And it suggests that many concepts have dimensions of significance and relationship that are not indicated by a diagram such as Margenau's.

The question might now be asked where the conceptual inter-relations and interactions of science with its environment appear in the three-ring diagram of Fig. 2.* The answer is that as it stands they don't. This is a scheme for depicting the conscious and deliberate activities of the science community; and neither the incipient forming nor the subsequent appropriation of presuppositional meanings is in essence a planned activity. Rather it is unconscious or subconscious, a "seeing" or receiving, an inheritance or gift—on the one hand an infiltration into science from the common understandings, and on the other an uncontrived flow from science into the common understandings.

All this constitutes one of the environmental aspects of community to which we referred briefly in Chapter IV. To depict it schematically we might then—in our imagination—extend Fig. 2 by drawing around the threefold diagram a series of radial arrows, some pointing inward toward the "scientific circle" and alternate ones pointing outward from it. We would then be indicating that the three-fold enterprise of science does not exist in isolation, but operates in and is an integral part of an all pervading culture. The inward arrows would suggest that science is affected in its thinking by the thought patterns of its surroundings. The outward ones would imply that the culture receives, as well as gives, and is itself in part the product of scientific thought. Similar remarks apply to religion also—and for that matter to all parts of the cognitive spectrum, to all fields of inquiry leading to knowledge. For all of them there are interrelations and interactions among concepts. All of them have presuppositional elements.

* See p. 69.

CHAPTER XI

Interactions of Faiths and Myths

What of the Future?

1 · TURNING A CORNER

Throughout this book we have stressed the idea that to understand science—and religion for that matter—in all aspects of its nature and significance, one must think of it not only in terms of ideas, but of human relations and values. Consistent with this point of view, we early in our argument emphasized the fact that science involves not only knowledge, but faith—in nature, in certain intellectual procedures (scientific method), and in the science community. Now, having in the preceding chapter considered the interactions between the conceptual understandings of science and of its environment, we should extend the analysis to take into account those involving their faiths. In the great maze of communal and cultural interrelations not only are men's knowledge and understandings operative, but so are their confidence, commitments, and loyalties.

Perhaps the best way to point up our inquiry and concern is to ask some questions about the future. One ingredient or concomitant of faith is confident hope. Is there any reasonable ground for hope that the future of mankind will be worth living, i.e., make sense in terms of ultimate values? It is a fact of our times that men are looking into the future with great anxiety and fear. It has become trite to remark that science has given man unprecedented power of control over his environment, but not over himself; that he is in the unenviable situation of now being able utterly to destroy himself and his world, without any assurance that he will not actually do it. As man in this predicament looks about for a source of help and of courage, what does he find? Is there any meaningful end toward which he and the world are moving, any discernible cosmic purpose? Are science and religion likely to play any significant role in all this?

We should realize, of course, that in asking such questions we are turning a corner. Thus far we have engaged in interpretive description of the actualities of the past and present of science and religion. Now we are proposing to consider the possibilities and probabilities of their future. Before proceeding, then, it may be well to review what our strategy has been relative to the purpose of this book.

2 · MY STRATEGY THUS FAR

It has been my intention to lay a foundation for the more important—and much more difficult—business of relating science and religion meaningfully and positively in our culture. I have felt that to be satisfactory the relationship to be achieved must seem reasonable and significant, not only to a relatively few professional apologists and systematic bridge builders trying to connect the two, but to the rank and file of intelligent people. Moreover, it must be a natural, not forced, solution, one that is not only *thinkable,* but *workable.* But this means in turn that the synthesis that is needed must be much more than a philosophic tour-de-force contrived by experts,* and that it must come out of the life and thought of many people working out their destiny together in the realities of actual life.

Some years ago John Mackay said this much better by referring to two perspectives, that of the Balcony and that of the Road. The former offers the detached point of view, the look from above the jostling traffic on the highway. The latter, on the other hand,

---

* Indeed I have elsewhere expressed the view that any attempt to achieve synthesis by means of an all-inclusive philosophic *system* must fail.[1] Robert Oppenheimer has put it this way: "The unity of culture . . . cannot be an architectonic unity, . . . it cannot have the architectural coherence of a hierarchy." In discussing how to achieve the unity we seek he suggests: "We can have each other to dinner. We ourselves, and with each other by our converse, can create, not an architecture of global scope, but an immense intricate network of intimacy, illumination, and understanding."[2] See also his *Science and the Common Understanding.*[3]

stands for participation, "the place where life is tensely lived, where thought has its birth in conflict and concern, where choices are made and decisions carried out. It is the place of action, of pilgrimage, of crusade, where concern is never absent from the wayfarer's heart. On the Road a goal is sought, dangers are faced, life is poured out." [4] Mackay suggested that to attain truth—truth that matters—one must descend from the Balcony to the Road. And this is what I am saying here. The working out of a genuine, truly integrating, and existentially meaningful synthesis of science and religion will require both perspectives, but especially the Road. If it is to have meaning for the man on the Road, it must be related to the concerns that come out of life on the Road, and include insights gained there.

"Let us beware, however," says Mackay, "lest we interpret the Road in a purely physical sense. Many have passed their lives on the Road who never journeyed very far from their desk or pulpit; from a hospital clinic or a carpenter's bench. Others serve upon the Road 'who only stand and wait.' For the Road, like the Balcony, is a state of the soul." [5] Wherever, then, men and women talk about science and religion with deep concern and not only out of superficial curiosity, in the class room or study, the bull session or the forum, the church or the political arena, the foxhole or the home, *there* is where the synthesis will be forged—if at all.

All too often, however, the talk is about a science or religion that does not exist or is misconceived. Too often the conversation is earnest but uninformed. This is why I have felt the need for a more satisfactory foundation for such conversation, namely a more adequate conception of the nature of science and religion—in their existential realities. And this is why I have tried to stress their human and communal aspects, and some of their relations to our culture.

3 · WHITHER MANKIND? IMMEDIATE CONCERNS

The question now is, In what kinds of settings are such conversations likely to take place in the future, and in the face of what sorts of problems are the relationships of science and religion apt to be forged? The query, What of the Future? may also be put, perhaps more significantly, as Whither Mankind? This question has at least two aspects, one pertaining to our immediate concerns, our daily physical and social needs and well being, and the other to our ultimate ones, having to do with ultimate meaning, mystery, and destiny—with life lived in depth.

The immediacies of the future will no doubt be determined largely by advances in the basic and applied sciences. Some of these we can foresee. While today's world is dominated by the physical sciences, as indicated by nuclear energy, space exploration, and automation, that of tomorrow will probably belong to biology. Already it has achieved remarkable insight into the nature of biological life and death. From this, and much more to come, will be developed greatly improved plant and animal resources, and much more effective control of disease. Human genetics will probably yield extensive pre-natal control of the characteristics of human offspring. Artificial insemination is even now a reality, and human conception without the male element is not, some biologists tell us, an utter impossibility. Biochemists are already inundating us with many remarkable drugs for transforming human personality and for inducing a variety of states of mind, and we can expect many more.

Perhaps after the biologically conditioned world will come one fashioned by the psychologists and psychosocial engineers, i.e., by the psycho-manipulators of men. Without doubt it will be an era of epoch-making discoveries concerning the human psyche, and of further developments in psychosomatics, the science of the inter-relations of mental and physical states.

Some time, perhaps surprisingly soon, there may be quite unexpected developments, possibly the discovery and exploration of vast realms of reality now utterly unknown to us—the discovery of which may not only radically alter our present conceptions of reality. Some break-throughs may well come in the physical sciences, opening up worlds as strange, seemingly, as was electricity when it was first discovered, or as radioactivity, the exploration of which has led us inside the nucleus of the atom and brought on the atomic age. Some will surely come in biology. Thus many scientists are confident that before long it will be possible in the laboratory to combine certain chemical substances under critical conditions to produce a bio-chemical compound endowed with life. And this neo-life might conceivably have potentials for evolution quite different from anything now known.

There could be unprecedented break-throughs in the social sciences, especially if these sciences could turn their attention more than in the past to the investigation of the more distinctive characteristics of man as distinguished from those of the animals. More than twenty-five years ago, no less a prophet than John Dewey pointed out, what is still largely true, that the psychology of the most characteristically and distinctively human does not yet exist. I am assured by experts on the subject that the same can be said even now of sociology, economics and political science. Theory in these fields seems as yet strangely inadequate and inapplicable to actual existence. Its predictive models of man are still far from including all of those significant factors that distinguish man from the animal or the machine. When, however, these sciences become more truly the sciences of *humanity,* when they have succeeded in plumbing the primal depths of the human psyche at the levels of the nonrational and transrational even below those uncovered by Freud, they are sure to add important new dimensions to the scientific vision of man and of the cosmos, and to disclose what even the poets, novelists, dramatists and prophets have not yet dreamed of.

If these forecasts are at all accurate, there will be a vast transformation not only in man's physical environment and mode of public life, but in his private *inner life.* To say the very least, I suspect there will be forced upon him radical changes in his very ways of thinking, his intellectual tools, his methods of investigating and evaluating many aspects of life and the world. Observe, for instance, the impact even now upon scholarship and technology of our modern computers and cybernetic devices—devices .that enable us to solve problems very far beyond the capacity of the unaided human brain, involving many variables and boundary conditions. Problems, such as those encountered in the difficult field of crystal-structure analysis, that would just a few years ago have required four or five years of work on the part of a team of computing analysts, can now be solved in a few hours or days by a single individual. Meteorology, the science of the weather, which in its analytic and predictive function has always been handicapped by its inability to cope with large numbers of variables and data, is being completely transformed by the advent of modern computers. And the social sciences, which have always had to deal with a larger number of variables than have the physical sciences, have likewise been benefited by the incredibly powerful methods of handling data.

But these new thinking aids are useful not only for the realms of quantitative analysis and prediction, but for those that are basically more qualitative, such as classifying, comparing, translating, and for various kinds of controls. Moreover they enlarge our creative capacities, for instance in the composition of music. This may mean a great deal more for the arts than we now realize.

If a child were to be born with the capacity to solve problems a thousand times more difficult in a thousandth of the time required by an ordinary child, we would marvel. If he potentially had the power, or could develop it, for turning out a full-length symphony in a few hours, and several radically different kinds of musical compositions in a day or two, we might well say that something new had emerged in the evolution of man. But, I suggest, this has already happened. The generation now being born will in this sense be a virtually new species, with incredibly amplified abilities and capacities acquired not only through biological heredity but much more through cultural heredity, i.e., through the technological amplification of the ability to think, analyze, predict, decide, and create.

4 · WHITHER? ULTIMATE CONCERNS

Thinking further about changes in man's inner life, we may expect radical changes also in man's basic understanding of, or capacity for, truth, beauty and goodness, love and justice, as well as their opposites, and in his relation to ultimate reality. And if so, these will occur in a setting of unprecedented problems relating to our ideals and value systems, our ethics and morals, our aesthetic and religious commitments, our basic faith out of which come our motivations and convictions.

How legitimate is human engineering, the deliberate tampering with, the control or modification of, the bodies, minds and characters of unborn children, or of children and adults already on the scene? How are we going to decide whether it is or is not? Will the traditional criteria and understandings suffice as guides? If not legitimate on moral grounds, how could it be prevented in the face of the terrific pressures of research and development producing techniques for doing it? If legitimate in principle, how could it be protected from exploitation by the unscrupulous? And, what is perhaps even more important, how would we know what is really best in particular cases?

In what ways will all this affect society? The family and the home? Would the words father, mother, son, and daughter still have significant meaning? Would there remain any real freedom—for individual, or community, or nation? How utterly might it transform our conceptions of right and wrong, the honorable and dishonorable, the loyal and disloyal, and patriotism? Could the God concept survive, or the basic experience of faith?

Clearly, then, we have shifted attention from the immediate to the ultimate aspects of the question What of the Future?—to questions about freedom or bondage, hope or despair, love or hatred, life or death, being or nonbeing.

Now, traditionally such questions in their ultimate significance have been considered the province not of science, but of religion. Indeed, as we have seen, religion is conceived by many contemporary thinkers as the realm of ultimate concern and values, whereas science is said to have only preliminary ones. In recent decades, however, by an almost imperceptible, subtle, but very real process of extension and transmutation, the concerns and preoccupations of science, broadly conceived, have come to include certain ultimate ones—especially those pertaining to the question of human destiny. Whether we like this development or not, we must, I think, accept it as an accomplished fact, and, if we are wise, try to make the most of it. What I am referring to is the fact that men, both inside and outside the science community, feel that out of science has come a new and powerful faith, a saving faith, that has given them a new basis for hope and confidence in the future, and that this faith is now regarded by them as integral to science itself. There are two aspects of this faith that we should consider.

The first comes basically out of the scientific insight that nature is orderly and predictable, and can be controlled at least to some extent, and the second out of the concept and perspective of evolution.

5 · TWO ASPECTS OF THE COMMON "SCIENTIFIC" FAITH

The first of these is also twofold. Science has given us a feeling of confidence and security deriving from the conviction that nature is not only a cosmos rather than a chaos and that things happen for good cause-and-effect reasons, but that it is not subject to the intervention of "spiritual hosts of wickedness in the heavenly places" [6]—or even of an arbitrarily acting God. For vast numbers of people, angels, demons, ghosts, and witches no longer exist. Nor does a personal God who allows misfortunes to overtake people or who banishes them to hell fire as punishment for their evil deeds. The basis for what they would consider to be superstitious fears has been removed.*

When Christianity went forth into the world to preach the Gospel, an important part of it was the "good news" that the power of the demonic hosts had been conquered by Christ. Nevertheless for many centuries in the minds of men, even Christians, these "hosts," conceived as personal, spiritual beings with certain powers over nature and men, continued to exist, had to be reckoned with, and were feared. Not until modern science came along were men's minds and hearts finally liberated from this bondage.† It is but natural therefore that science is credited with having provided mankind with the basis for a new faith with which men can look into the future with considerable confidence.

The second aspect of this "scientific" faith derives, justifiably or unjustifiably, from the scientific concept of evolution, and more immediately from the mythological concept of *Evolution with a*

* The point here is not whether angels and demons exist or not, or whether science is able to prove or disprove their existence, but that as a matter of fact out of the scientific experience of mankind there has emerged the conviction shared by large segments of mankind that they do not exist.

† This liberation has of course not yet been completed throughout the world, or even among civilized people. But it seems evident that wherever science goes, liberation follows.

capital E [7] regarded as purposive cause and as a determinant of cosmic destiny.

6 · ABOUT MYTH

Before proceeding with this let us parenthetically discuss the term "myth." As commonly understood, a myth is an untrue story. One commonly says, "Oh, that is only a myth," meaning a fancied rather than true account. Though this is a standard usage of the word, it is not the only one, and not the one I am employing here. According to one standard meaning, a myth is that literary form that is peculiarly suitable for the expression of the most basic and deepest faith-belief insights of a culture.[8] It is, of course, related to *mythos,* which is defined by Professor Bernard Meland as "the pattern of meaning and valuations which has been imaginatively projected through drama or metaphor, expressing the perceptive truths of the historic experience of a people, bearing upon man's nature and destiny." [9] A myth is then a particular symbolic structure of narrative imagery that expresses something eminently true. It says what is known but cannot be conveyed by more ordinary ways of speech. Many Old Testament scholars regard the first eleven chapters of Genesis as myth in this sense, as contrasted with chapters twelve to fifty, that are seen as legend, and certain other parts of the Bible that are history.[10] Having noted earlier that the first pages of the Bible are not to be taken literalistically, but symbolically, we now add that they should be regarded more specifically as mythical.

Philip Wheelwright has spoken with great insight about "man's threshold existence." He points out that "man lives always on the borderland of something more" with "the intimation of something more, a beyond the horizon. . . . To be conscious is not just to be; it is to mean, to intend, to point beyond oneself, to testify that some kind of beyond exists, and to be ever on the verge of entering it." [11] In developing this theme he speaks of the "threshold of time," the "threshold of the world," and the "threshold of the unseen." It is because man's life extends into this realm of threshold existence that it has become necessary for him to devise the method of communicating by means of symbols and metaphors, or myths.

And with myths he communicates his deepest and most precious insights, those associated with his deepest concerns and faiths, those that come out of this threshold experience. This is why myths deal with the perennial and momentous questions of whence and whither, life and death, and the origin of good and evil.

Now most myths have in the past been cast in anthropomorphic imagery. As Stephen Toulmin has suggested, however, there have come into being twentieth century myths that are mechanomorphic and make use of scientific imagery and concepts.[12] One of these modern myths in western culture is that of *Evolution with a capital E*. As Toulmin has suggested with great cogency, this myth expresses beliefs that are not verifiable scientifically and go far beyond the findings of either direct or indirect observation of evolution (with a lower case *e*) in laboratory or field. As I see it, it comes more out of the twentieth century's faith derived from science, than from scientific knowledge itself. It is, of course, difficult to distinguish between the belief and faith aspects of this myth. But this seems to be true of all genuine myths.

It should be said finally that a myth is not constructed at will or by a process of deliberate intellectual creation, or by logical development. Rather it comes gradually and unpremeditatedly out of the depth of cultural consciousness and experience, as in that culture men find or are given faith. And it is equally true, I think, that the faith grows as the myth grows—another circular relationship.

7 · TWO MYTHS AND FAITHS

It is well known that according to evolutionary conceptions man is the culmination of a long development from earlier forms of life, and of still earlier developments in the inanimate world. While this evolutionary process is thought of as a continuous one, there seem to be good reasons for thinking that the curve of change has discontinuities in it when extraordinary things happen, e.g., when there are unpredictable mutations, or "changes of state." * One

---

* The notion of change of state has been applied to the evolutionary process with considerable ingenuity by Father Teilhard de Chardin in his remarkable book, *The Phenomenon of Man*.[13]

such discontinuity yielded living organisms. During a later one the human mind and spirit emerged. It seems to be recognized increasingly that when man appeared on earth there emerged a creature with truly novel characteristics. For one thing, unlike his progenitors he has been able to look at himself and his genesis self-consciously, and in time to recognize himself as an outcome of the evolutionary process. More than that, he had the potential for consciously transforming his physical environment as well as creating a new kind of environment called culture, and thus causally determining in part his further evolution. Along with this, he has the remarkable faculty of discerning that there exist also cosmic determinants beyond his comprehension and control. And finally, with his genesis there appeared the capacity for ultimate concern and commitment, for unprecedented love and hatred, and para-doxically for the creating of community based on common faith, loyalty and love, or for destroying it. While man certainly is re-lated organically to the animals, there can be no doubt that with respect to these mental-spiritual qualities he is a new being very different from them.

This over-all picture of "development" is a rather impressive one, not only in magnitude and splendor, but also in direction. In terms of values current in our culture today, this evolutionary trend must be regarded as "upward," from lesser to higher values. The development from elementary particles to atoms, to molecules, to molecular chains endowed with life, to cells and microorganisms, to large plants and animals, and finally to man and social struc-tures, has been seen as an upward tendency, from bare simplicity toward rich complexity, increasing organization, mutuality, and self-consciousness; from the inanimate to life, to mind, and spirit; from individual to group, to community, to civilization. While many have not interpreted this process as having a goal and purpose, others have—and what is more, they regard it as a *good* goal and purpose. For them it has given meaning to much that formerly seemed pur-poseless and without significance. Cosmic order and predictability, conceived largely in terms of cause-and-effect relationships, have thus been seen to have also the dimension of telic order. A few of those who have given expression to this sort of outlook are Henri Bergson, Julian Huxley, Edmund W. Sinnott [14] and Teilhard de

Chardin. While there are among them many differences as to details of the picture, in its main features they seem to see very much alike.

This vision has entered the realm of common understandings. Men who are not at all expert in regard to the particularities of *evolution* have come to feel it in their bones, i.e., intuitively, that this picture makes a great deal of sense, and says something very important and meaningful in regard to the nature of man and the world. In this way there has come into being a new, modern myth, that of *Evolution,* which expresses what many men regard as truths. While these go far beyond anything at present verifiable by scientific methods, they seem to be consistent with, and the not illogical extrapolations of, the more strictly scientific picture of *evolution.* Not only is it a grand story, but it is a pattern of meanings and evaluations, to use Meland's phrase, and an expression of a deep and powerful faith and hope. For it is not only a perspective of the past, but a vision of the future. And according to some of its more optimistic interpreters the eventual future envisioned is a "new earth" brought about by the final triumph of good over evil. This then is what is coming to be the "scientific" myth and faith of our time.

Now let us turn to religion, and particularly to the religion of the West. As we have seen, it also has given us a mythos, in the sense of a pattern of meaning and valuations having to do with the origin, nature, and destiny of man, namely the biblical Judaeo-Christian story. It too sees purpose in the cosmos, and progress toward a goal; from a dark earth "without form and void" to light and matter, to life, to human spirit, and to a "new earth" and holy city (community). In some respects this older myth seems to me to be much more adequate and realistic than the newer one. First, it recognizes much more explicitly not only the goodness of man but his power of destruction and his predilection for demonic evil, his urges toward righteousness and toward sin. Second, it sees with great clarity the reality and power of trans-human, divine grace as the ultimate determinant of destiny. Within this pattern Christianity sees the Christ as the structure of new being and the promise of the ultimate triumph of creative and redemptive love.

Both myths have at times been interpreted deterministically— as though the eventual outcome hoped for were positively assured

and inevitable. This determinism appeared respectively in the belief in "progress" [15] and the doctrine of divine predestination. But
these no longer seem convincing—if they ever did. Virtually everybody seems to realize now, from either a scientific or religious
point of view—or both—that man is so constituted that it is not at
all unlikely that he may ruthlessly destroy himself and the world.
Who can doubt that he has the power and techniques, as well as
the irresponsible inclinations and the freedom to do it almost at
will? And yet there is withal a basic faith expressed by both myths
that the "gates of hell shall not prevail."

Faith together with myth is not only an attitude and pattern of
meaning, but a channel of power. To put it in somewhat more
theological language, it is through faith that self-transcending love
can be released among men for redemptive action. Unfortunately,
however, in spite of what I have just said about the finding of a
new faith and the vigorous resurgence of old ones, on the whole our
western world has for some time been in danger of losing all faith,
and if it does the forces of evil leading to chaos and extinction will
be unopposed. One exceedingly potent reason for this ominous
circumstance is that the two faiths we have spoken of, the so-called
"scientific" and the religious, have been interpreted as being opposed
in their ultimate implications. But may this not be an unnecessary
or perhaps even false interpretation?

8 · SOME QUERIES AND ISSUES

The two mythical stories that express these two faiths are obviously remarkably alike in many respects: in the over-all picture
they present of the sequence of happenings they envisage, the beginning and final end, the whence and whither of mankind. It
seems clear to me that they are also gradually converging with regard to both their conception of the nature of man and of cosmic
history. On the science side there is a growing recognition, first,
that man is more than he was formerly conceived to be scientifically, and second, that the whole of reality comprehends more than
is accessible through scientific methods. On the side of religion
there seems to me to be an explicit recognition of the validity of
scientific knowledge, much assiduous analyzing of religious con-

cepts to identify their experiential meaning, and a search for more appropriate meaningful symbols for the expression of fundamental insights.

Why then should they be regarded as inimical? Where are the issues? There are, of course, many and we shall not be able to look at them all individually. There is one, however, that implies most of them and has been identified by Roger Hazelton as central. He says, "The most weighty" issue for the future conversation between scientists and theologians "has to do with the meaning of the word 'nature' itself. . . . Is nature to be regarded as a 'nothing but' category, an all-embracing and all-sufficient synonym for everything there is, or is it rather the case that we can only include nature, in the sense of 'the way things are,' by a principle of understanding that transcends it as well? . . . There is . . . no quarrel with science as to what the facts are; the whole issue raised by theology concerns what the facts mean." Do the scientifically verifiable facts about nature necessarily signify that nature is a self-originating, self-perpetuating, self-operating entity or system governed merely by chance, or may they be regarded as interpretable by the concept of nature as a creation willed by God? May nature be regarded also, as Hazelton asks, "as a sacrament of God, . . . somehow capable of showing forth its divine origin, . . . eminently alive, . . . and capable of making response on many levels . . . to the ground of its being"? The question at issue, he suggests, is, "Can the scientist and the theologian agree in principle on this conception of nature as open upward to God?" [16]

Is it not likely that the answer to this important question, or the resolution of this issue, will depend, at least in part, upon what content the theologians will insist must be given to such concepts as "divine origin" and "God"? May it not be then that Hazelton has formulated only half of "the most weighty" issue, and that the other half has to do with the meaning of the word "God"? Is *it* to be regarded in a restrictive and exclusive way, and as a "nothing but" category? A very able theologian has said that whenever scientists write about religion, without exception they assume a pantheistic position. As I see it, however, some of these writers are doing rather original thinking, using thought patterns that simply do not fit into the traditional categories. May it not be that the usual labels, like *theist, deist, pantheist, naturalist, supernaturalist,* and many other traditional symbols for talking about God no longer convey clearcut meaning and are therefore inadequate for use in contemporary conversation between scientist and theologian, or for that matter with humanist and philosopher? As has been suggested repeatedly of recent years, we may need a new name for God, as well as new ways of thinking about Him. Should we not have a more distinctive pronoun for referring to God, one obviating the necessity of choosing between *Him* and *It?* Perhaps it should suggest that God may not be either He or It, but He *and* It *and* very much more than these traditional pronouns can possibly imply. Is it not conceivable that the myth of Evolution may make at least a partial contribution in the direction of a more meaningful symbolism?

May it not be that present conflicts represent for the most part a clash of symbols rather than of basic faiths? If we were to demythologize them, i.e., penetrate beneath the symbols to their fiducial and fideistic referents, might they not turn out to be in accord? Complementary rather than mutually exclusive? Might it not even turn out that these apparently separate faiths are at heart but different aspects of one faith—the faith in One God, the God beyond the gods, Being itself—and that their attendant myths represent but different views or perspectives of the same cosmic and historical scene of experience, reality and insight?

But there is quite another issue also. Not only has a powerful new cosmic faith come out of science, but science has itself become the object of faith, a god to be depended on and adored. This is understandable, since mankind is deeply in debt to science, not only for technological but for intellectual and spiritual blessings. Moreover, if our predictions for the future come true, science will affect and shape our lives even more than it does now. If it does this beneficently it may for many people become even more of a god than at present. To complicate the situation, there is also the possibility that science may become self-centered, finding the focus of its interests, concerns and faith within itself, in its conceptual structures, its intellectual processes, its communal power. This is a typical human danger to which all movements, enterprises and communities are subject more or less, including institutional religion.

Concerning this kind of situation I should like to quote H. Richard Niebuhr. "When I reflect on the present human situation it is the problem of faith that presents itself to me as of the greatest importance; and faith is to be distinguished from religion . . . . our whole culture is involved in a conflict of faiths that is distinctly different from the collisions among religions or between religion and irreligion." Then he identifies the most ominous conflict as that between monotheism and henotheism, i.e., any "social faith which makes a finite society, whether cultural or religious, the object of trust as well as of loyalty." [17] To make the enterprise or community of science the object of one's highest trust and loyalty may be to adopt a henotheistic faith. Certainly it is to believe in a finite god that parallels or coexists with many other gods or idols, such as democracy, race, nation, business, and institutional religion.

Thus we are reminded that the *most* fundamental issue is after all not one of conception and belief, but of faith, loyalty and hope. Where can we most reliably anchor our faith and confidence? And it is by being related to this prior concern that the question of conception and belief becomes truly important. From that point of view the question we discussed earlier becomes: What conception of the divine will make our choice of an object of faith most meaningful, and open our minds and hearts most completely to the God beyond our conceptions and beyond the gods of henotheism? When formulated in this way the issue takes on a different hue, and becomes more like one encountered on the Road rather than the Balcony. It is the question the common man is asking. It is an existential choice as well as an academic one that must be made—one made urgent by the perplexities of the incredible revolution in our way of life that faces us in the immediate future.

9 · SCIENCE AS DESTROYER OF FAITH

It is a curious but very real fact of life that while for many people science generates intense faith, for many others it is the cause of deep doubt, despair and anxiety. This subject too has many facets, only a few of which we can consider here.

First, there is the so-called dehumanizing influence of science, i.e., its alleged preoccupation with material things, subservience to technology, eagerness to profit from war or, and more fundamentally, from its ethical neutrality. The pessimism and despair displayed here seem to be, at least in part, conceptual in origin, stemming from inadequate interpretations that depict science as utterly impersonal and inhumanely uninterested in values. In part also it is nonconceptual, stemming from primal, "visceral" reactions to the pressures of a technological culture, e.g., the growing dominance of life by gadgetry, the threat of automation and the displacement of human labor, the artificialities or urban life, the mechanization of the arts, and the stifling of the individual by collectivism.

The second facet is related to the first, though certainly different from it. It has been called by Professor Max Born the "tragic fusion of physics and politics" [18] which has resulted in what is considered to be the loss of freedom and integrity by science, and has greatly multiplied the probability of cataclysmic disaster in the future.

A third consideration, also related to the first, is that science and technology have greatly altered the very foundation of existence by utterly changing the landscape. Somewhere a distinguished scientist * has said that virtually everything that seems most significant and indispensable to man as he looks out upon the visible world is man-made: factories and dams, powerlines, transportation and communication systems, homes and palaces of business, warehouses, schools and churches. Even food and fibre for clothing are to an astonishing extent man-made. Man himself seems therefore to be his only important source of support. If he fails he can turn to no other. Thus he is utterly alone—in an indifferent, uninterested universe. He can have faith only in himself, and for many men this is quite intolerable.

Fourth, the insistence of many scientists that science can find

* My memory is that it was Werner Heisenberg who said this, although I seem unable to put my finger on the reference.

no purpose in the universe, and the shift from determinism to the reign of probability and chance in physical theory, have for many men transformed the cosmos of earlier conceptions into what is again essentially a chaos without meaning. There is for them no basis for a belief and faith in cosmic purpose.

Next, man seems to many observers to have lost status and significance in the universe. For them the greatly expanded conception of the stellar universe has made the earth and man seem progressively smaller and more insignificant in the totality of things. This, together with the much-proclaimed eventual thermodynamic death of the world, seems to have robbed many men of all hope in any meaningful future and therefore of any meaning now.

That these views and feelings are very widespread today is amply shown by contemporary existentialist philosophy, literature, and art, which depict man as completely torn and distorted by anxiety and shorn of all hope. Thus there are in our contemporary culture not only devastating tensions between competing faiths, but between faith and despair. For many neither science nor religion seems adequate as antidote to the poisons of desolating despair that seem abroad in our culture today and seem to incapacitate us. To many the horrors of George Orwell's prophecy, *1984,* and Aldous Huxley's two on the *Brave New World,*[19] seem all but inevitable.

10 · THE EXISTENTIAL WEB

In many ways, then, science interacts with religion and with our culture at the level of faith, as well as that of belief. Here it touches upon man's greatest needs and concerns, and it is perhaps in this realm that it is destined to influence mankind most in the future. One of the most perplexing aspects of this situation, however, is the inconsistency of men's reactions to science: as we have seen, in some cases boundless faith and in others hopeless despair.

In part these questions of faith come out of problems of belief. In part they relate to the symbols used in expressing faith and belief. In part also they arise from men's individual experiences and existential relationships to the world, their fellow men and their God or gods. There are many strands in the web of human existence, all of them connected directly or indirectly: thought and deed, belief and faith, doubt and despair, knowledge and understanding; the personal and impersonal; individual, community and culture; matter, mind, and spirit; myth, legend and history; love and loyalty, hate and infidelity, sacrifice and devotion. Science and religion are both inextricably enmeshed in this all-inclusive web. Somehow we must learn how to both fashion and interpret them so that each will contribute to the strength, beauty and utility of the whole fabric.

CHAPTER XII

Pluralism and Relativism

In Conclusion

1 · SOME FACTS OF THE CASE

No comparative study of science and religion would be complete if it omitted reference to the perplexing phenomenon of religious pluralism and relativism. It is well known that there are many religions and that they make conflicting truth-claims about God, nature and man, aside from other kinds of claims and demands on which they disagree. The question is in what sense this can or cannot be said to be the case actually, what it signifies, and finally how it can be so. Apparently there is nothing like it in science. Why not? Does it imply that "truth" is relative and pluralistic in religion, while in science it is not? It would of course not be appropriate to the purposes and scope of this book to undertake in it an exhaustive treatment of this difficult subject. I shall therefore consider it here only to the extent to which it can contribute further to our understanding of the nature of science and religion.

Perhaps the first point to be noted is that there is another fact quite as puzzling as the multiplicity and variety of religions, namely the astounding universality and perenniality of religion (in the singular). Indeed the phenomenon of religion in the life and thought of mankind is at least as impressive in this regard as is that of science. Men of all races and cultures have claimed with surprising unanimity an awareness of the holy and divine, have responded to it in faith, prayer and worship, have felt impelled to entrust and commit themselves to it. Everywhere men have been conscious of ethical and moral demands emanating from it. One of the most widely propagated and universally prevailing concepts is that of "God," in whatever linguistic garb it may appear.

It is evident, of course, that in speaking of these phenomena we are referring to the experiential, empirical component of religion that is represented by circle *a* of the three-ring diagram (Fig. 2),* to the common experiences of mankind listed in column A of Table VI,† and to the findings of Otto, Heiler, Underhill and Eliade, to whom we referred earlier,‡ and to many other investigators. And in mentioning the concept of "God" in this particular connection, reference is in part to "God A" (Chapter IX), to that component of meaning we have designated as meaning-by-empirical analysis, which meaning can come only out of the kind of phenomenological analyses that the scholars just mentioned have carried out. In part reference is also to "God B" by virtue of the fact that vast numbers of sensitive men of many faiths, common men who have never heard of such critical analyses, have testified that they have individually been keenly conscious (intuitively) of being in the presence of holy reality.

It is especially significant for present purposes that when men of different faiths engage in worship together—in temple or foxhole or concentration camp—they often come to realize convincingly that they are worshipping the same holy reality, the same God, and that out of such experiences comes also a surprising degree of understanding and appreciation of faiths other than their own. Sometimes such understanding is then put into eloquent words so that others can at least to some extent share it. A rather convincing example of this is presented by Huston Smith's remarkable book *The Religions of Mankind*.[1] That this is a work of genuine scholarship is obvious. But it is equally obvious that it is more than that, for it reveals dimensions of understanding far beyond those that characterize the dispassionate, ivory tower kind of study required in such disciplines as, say, *comparative religion* and *philosophy of religion*. There is also a warm-hearted—as well as cold, hard-headed—recognition of something tremendous at the heart of all high religions, and those called low, that makes

* See diagram, p. 69.
† See pp. 158–159.
‡ See Notes for Chapter IX.

them kin under God. And what it helps us to realize is that to an impressive extent mankind is *one* in its "experience of God," in its intuitive apprehension of God, and in its knowing God as one who is good and is to be worshipped, adored, obeyed, and served. To speak then of religious pluralism or relativism in sweeping terms without qualifications would be seriously to misrepresent the situation. The fact to be remarked first is man's unity and unanimity in both the intuitive-presuppositional awareness of God ("God B") and the analyzable and describable experience of God ("God A"). Happily, once this fundamental fact of unity is seen clearly, the second and equally evident one of pluralistic variety and diversity begins to make some sense and seem less perplexing.

For one thing, when we look carefully at the latter, what seems to stand out in bold relief and to strike the eye with special force is that the competitive aspects of the diversity apparent among the religions of the world lies for the most part in their theological teachings, in the area of theological conceptions and postulations, i.e., in column C of Table VI. As one reflects upon the entries in column A one gets the impression that while there are differences also, i.e., in their experiential aspects, these differences represent different historical opportunities and perhaps different rates of growth and maturation, different degrees of sensitivity and response to the divine, but not occasions for or causes of exclusive, argumentative and controversial claims. It is when one contemplates the entries in column C that the divisive, competitive and imperialistic effects of pluralism show up. In the main it is with regard to "God C" that the religions hurl most of their charges and countercharges. Why?

2 · WHY SHOULD PLURALISM BE EXPECTED?

In considering the problems arising from this situation we can again distinguish two kinds, those of an attitudinal or emotional nature, and those that are more substantive. Let us scrutinize the latter first and ask why there should be this variety of ways of thinking about God. This is not intended as a metaphysical why-question that is answerable in terms of a "first cause," but rather as a how-question of the kind that is asked in science and is answered by reference to observable cause-and-effect relations. From this point of view the proliferation per se of theological conceptions and systems should not be either surprising or objectionable. There are several lines of thought that suggest this, lines we have followed earlier in studying other problems.

To begin with, let us recall the spectrum of cognition discussed in Chapter X, and more especially the fact that as one passes from the physical to the social sciences the precise identification, mathematical treatment, and validation of facts become more difficult, and that for any given empirical situation competing explanations and theories become progressively more numerous. Thus while in astronomy and physics there are rarely more than two alternative theories for a particular subject at any time, there are many more in, say, psychology—witness for example the startling number of theories of learning. It should not therefore be altogether unexpected that in the rest of the spectrum, and especially in religion at its far end, the multiplicity of conceptual and theoretical structures should be even greater.

There are of course good reasons for this kind of difference between, say, theoretical physics and theology. For one thing, the task of theory in physics is much less complex. There is much less that needs to be explained or correlated theoretically. When the physicist looks out upon the cosmos and beholds its immense extent and complexity, and the huge number of kinds of objects, phenomena and relationships to be studied, he, like other scientists and scholars, comes to realize that as a whole it is beyond comprehension or analysis, and that any plumbing of its mystery and any forging of understanding can be achieved only by parts. He therefore confines his own quest to a special domain that his community has staked out for itself, thus deliberately disregarding most of what he sees and leaving its exploration to others.

Let the totality of existence be represented by a sphere consisting of concentric layers or shells, like an onion. When physicists look at the first, outer layer and find that this is where men claim to encounter the reality called God and the phenomena of righteousness and sin, they decide *qua* physicists that this is not their business. In the next they may see beauty, symmetry and rhythm, and then leave it for the artists. The next layers they may consign to the diplomats and politicians, the next to the historians, sociologists and psychologists. The phenomenon of life goes to the biologist, the mountains and oil deposits to the geologist and mineralogist. The layer of the constitution of matter is peeled off and given to the chemist. Finally the tiny core remaining at the center they claim as their own, a tiny sphere in which they are obliged to deal with only an extremely small fraction of the whole of reality, and where they encounter only the simplest of phenomena and the easiest of problems.* What this means, of course, is that they have deliberately and for valid strategic reasons ruled from their purview the most difficult and complicated areas of existence. No wonder their theories can be made to fit the facts with comparative ease. No wonder so few competing theories are needed or make their appearance. No wonder also that physics has been able to develop so successful a methodology and such easily verifiable theories.

We must recognize of course that this analogy of the concentric spherical shells is certainly imperfect and may get us into trouble if we push it too far. It should not, for instance, be interpreted to suggest that each discipline is limited strictly to its own shell. Rather the implication is that the problems of each discipline are more inclusive the farther out its layer is located in the sphere. Thus the biologist may not be able to solve his problems without taking into account physical and chemical factors and causes. The psychologist must in turn keep in mind not only the physical and chemical variables, but also the biological ones. And religious thought and theological theory must be prepared to cover all existence, to the extent that man's ultimate needs and concerns are affected by all components of reality and existence. On the other hand, things do not work this way in reverse. Thus the physicist need not in solving his problems take into account any of the factors associated specifically with the outer layers. While the

---

* It may be that the various sciences and arts should have been arranged in a somewhat different order along the radius of the sphere. In any case the order should be the same as in the spectrum of cognition, whatever the order. Moreover it must be remembered that in the outer layers especially there is much more overlapping and diffusion among layers. There the various fields cannot be differentiated as easily as they can nearer the center of the sphere.

biologist must of course reckon with physics and chemistry (the inner layers), he need not worry about sociology, history or art (the outer ones), when he is trying to solve his own problems. Without belaboring the matter further, the point of all this is that the tasks to be solved both empirically and theoretically in the more remote shells are much more complex and difficult than in the ones nearer the center. It is understandable therefore why in religion there should be more competing conceptual schemes than in science.

A second and more potent line of thought, suggesting that we should expect a pluralism of religious concepts and theories (C concepts-by-postulation), emerges from the fact that the historical experiences of different religious communities have in general been unlike in many ways—even though, as we have seen, in others they have been sufficiently alike to lead to an impressive degree of unanimity regarding the God concept. We should therefore recognize that there is as a matter of fact an altogether legitimate relativism * of religious beliefs, a relativity between belief and faith on the one hand, and historical experience, development and fact on the other. Christian theological conceptions are Christ-ian, i.e., determined so utterly by the revelation of God in Christ, because the Christian community has experienced and still remembers Christ. Jewish thought cannot be Christ-oriented or -determined because Jewish communal memory does not include the Christ event—and this applies, of course, to all non-Christian religions.† On the other hand, the concept of God as deliverer from bondage is held by the Jew and Christian at least in part because both communities regard the Exodus event as part of their history, part of that body of fact that their theological postulations are obliged to explain. Without pursuing this matter of historical rela-

* The meaning of historical relativism and its significance for theology has been expounded with great clarity by H. Richard Niebuhr in his *The Meaning of Revelation* and elsewhere.

† Any Christian objection at this point to the effect that "the Jews had the chance of accepting Christ but rejected him" would be beside the point. For whatever reasons, the Jewish community has not experienced the Christ, and therefore its concept of God cannot be and should not be expected to be Christ-determined. What may happen to individuals who leave the Jewish community to enter the Christian, or to those who leave the Christian community to join the Jewish, is quite another matter.

tivity further it should be clear that conceptual pluralism is inevitable where the historical experiences of peoples are very different.

Perhaps there is also a legitimate psychological relativism. I refer here to the types of individual experiences that are characteristic of different peoples, and especially to the variety of the quality and intensity of intuitional perception of and response to God. Especially notable here is the difference between the peoples of the East and of the West in this regard. In the thinking of the former the God concept seems to be dominated relatively more by the "God B" component-by-intuition than by the "God A" component-by-empirical analysis, while for the latter the emphasis is reversed. In the West historical experience and analytical thought are more determinative of theology than are the personal, mystical and non-rational experience and the non-conceptual elements of religion. Inevitably, then, religious thought and conceptual systems must be significantly different in East and West even though the basic insights they express may be much less so.

Third, and finally, the ways of thinking of divine reality would seem to vary necessarily from culture to culture because the masses of presuppositional material and the general thought patterns upon which they depend, as well as the mythical imagery and the symbols from everyday life that are available in them for religious language, create pressures toward different kinds of postulations and modes of conception.

It seems then that there are compelling reasons for the existence of pluralism of thought and doctrine in religion. While these and similar reasons apply much less in the social sciences and even less in the physical ones, they are by no means negligible, and they are certainly not altogether inoperative there. As we have seen, there *are* alternative or competing theories and interpretations in science at all times. But these usually apply to particular situations or problems and are more or less transient. They do not represent radically different points of view or conceptions of science. There have been, however, at times differences in scientific modes of thought and explanation that were so momentous as to justify the assertion that they represented different kinds of science as different as some of the religions.

I refer here not to any differences among theories in any of the contemporary sciences, or even to that which distinguishes Soviet science from so-called Western science, but rather to those that have been discovered by the relatively recent researches of such historians of science as Needham,[2] Price [3] and Neugebauer.[4] We have become so impressed by the successes of modern science, and by its monolithic and universal character, that it is difficult to visualize how there could be any other kind of science. Indeed there are those who assert that there is and can be only one, namely the one existing now throughout the world. It seems rather strange then to have so distinguished a scholar as Needham find that ancient Chinese science was radically different from contemporary science in both conception and method—and it was a real science, that disclosed many facts about nature, that gave us gunpowder and the magnetic compass, a very successful astronomy, and so on. Similarly, according to Neugebauer, Price and others, the ancient Babylonians had a remarkable astronomy which was radically different from Hellenic-Ptolemaic astronomy and yet was quite as successful in the prediction of the planetary motions. The Ptolemaic system was geometric, used spatial models by which the motions of the planets could be pictured, so to speak. The Babylonians, however, used a purely numerical system of prediction without any spatial models or concepts whatsoever. The Greek and the Babylonian schemes were not simply alternative theories subsumed under the same kind of science or the same way of thinking about nature. They represented two differently conceived sciences, as different as the modes of thought characterizing two different religions. There were still others.

It should be noted, of course, that here too we are talking about differences in conceptual schemes, differences in meaning-by-postulation corresponding to the entries of column C in Table V, and corresponding to "God C" of Table VI. The radical differences between the kinds of science we have noted lie in the main in the area of theory and interpretation. In regard to meanings-by-empirical analysis and -by-experience they are much more alike.

I believe that essentially the same causes have operated to bring about scientific pluralism as brought about religious pluralism. On the other hand there can be no doubt that in regard to the number of variants the pluralism of religion is of quite another order of magnitude. Today there is very little scientific pluralism. Why the variants of religion have persisted so long, while those of science have all but disappeared, is a question to which history may or may not be able to provide the answer. Perhaps it is because the particular forms of religious theory and interpretation, in terms of which the world and religious experience are explained and communicated, are less crucial to the attainment of truth and the other basic purposes of religion and faith than scientific theory is to the attainment of the purposes of science. Perhaps in matters of ultimate concern the particular forms of conceptualization and theory are less important than in matters of mere preliminary concern. Perhaps, to put it in more definitely religious terms, what God can do for man, and the faith relationship to God that man can have, are very much less dependent upon man's way of thinking theoretically than is man's relationship to nature. It may be that the necessities of the bonds binding religious faith, beliefs and symbolic system, are much less demanding, and the bonds more elastic, than are those of science. If this is true—and I myself have no doubt of it—it points to an existentially important difference in the nature of science and religion.

3 · ABERRATIONS AND ERRORS

If then it is not the pluralism of religion as such that is objectionable, it must be that it is some of its manifestations or concomitants, i.e., departures from the ideal, that are. This brings us back to the attitudinal and emotional aspects of the problem, which we must now consider. It is one of the darkest tragedies of human existence that the variety of religions has to so large an extent resulted in estrangement, exclusiveness, divisiveness, arrogance, intolerance, suspicion, hatred, fear, and *much bloodshed* —whereas it might, or should under God, have made for mutual enrichment and understanding, for inclusiveness and unity, for the elimination of oppression and war. It seems incredible that men would denounce, persecute and make war upon one another in the name of God. And yet this is just what they have done! One wonders which has been the greatest cause of bloodshed: unholy ambition to dominate other men or peoples, the avaricious lust for gold, or an intolerant "holy zeal for God"?

Yes, it must be admitted that existentially this has been the way of religions. This is in part their nature—in so far as they degenerate and become evil. Science has not displayed such horrors—at least not yet. But if science were to become a religion, as we have seen that it might, would it be any better? It is doubtful. There are no more built-in moral constraints in science than in religion, perhaps less. Why then have there been these degenerations and aberrations? Existentially the most pertinent answer from the viewpoint of Christian faith is *sin,* man's persistent tendency toward the subordination and domination of others, toward self-assertion and self-aggrandizement, and his forever wanting to throw off divine guidance and be or act like God.

This tendency shows up in the claim that the teachings of *one's own* religion (or sect) represent the truth about God and His will *while all others are definitely false,* that only through *one's own* religion can "salvation" be attained, that only through the pathway of *one's own* religion can mankind reach the "true God." Only through the sacred scriptures of *one's own* religion has God revealed Himself to man.

Not only does this tendency toward self-exaltation appear in the garb of exclusive claims for one's own religious beliefs and practices, but in the desire to impose these on others by compulsion—allegedly for their own good. History is so full of examples that are well known that we need not go into details regarding them here.

But aberrations due to sin are not the only cause of difficulty here. There are not a few others that are less vicious and may be put down as errors. Misplaced over-confidence in particular methodologies or institutions is a case in point. Sheer ignorance or lack of understanding of other teachings or points of view is another. No small amount of trouble arises from the failure to distinguish between what is experienced and what is postulated, what is factual and what is theoretical, between what God has revealed, and what man has supposed.

4 · CONFESSING AND LISTENING

What can be done in this situation? We can yield to the demands of God and accept His gracious gift of faith and love and let them displace our egocentric tendencies. We can come really to love our fellow men of other religions and faiths, eschewing the holier-than-thou attitude, recognizing that they too may be serving God—the same God.

In our religious thinking and theologizing we must give up defensiveness and aggressive argumentation as H. Richard Niebuhr has urged so persuasively,[5] and become confessional. We must become witnesses instead of warriors for our faith. And, as Huston Smith has suggested so eloquently,[6] we must listen—*listen to learn,* listen honestly. In confessing what we have learned we thus share our blessings with others. In listening to what others have learned we share in theirs.

Are then all religions equivalent or equal in meaning and value? relative to truth? with regard to goodness and holiness? Not at all. If our mutual confessing and listening are both honest and critical —as they must be—it will become evident that some insights and ways of life are less lofty than others in various ways, less near the true and the right. But there will be no invidious finger pointing. There will instead be much searching of one's own heart; no talk about which religion is the best, but much looking into the mirror in the attempt to remove the large obstruction in one's own eye rather than so much preoccupation with the tiny splinter in the neighbor's eye.

In our *confessing* we shall want to be good witnesses distinguishing carefully between what we have experienced and witnessed on the one hand, and what, on the other, we have concluded by putting two and two together in the constructions of our minds. Perhaps we shall discover that it is not our respective experiences that are contradictory so much as our interpretations. And perhaps we shall learn that variety in interpretations can be a positive good, that in time it can make for mutual enrichment under God of both experience and interpretation—and therefore of knowledge, truth and righteousness.

5 · A NOTE OF HOPE

May there not be hope in this: that we all learn "not that there is a God but that Being is God, or, better that the principle of being, the source of all things and the power by which they exist is good, is good for them and good to them." This is what Professor Niebuhr calls radical monotheism. "It is the confidence that whatever is, is good." [7]

For me the concrete meaning of this rather abstract assertion derives in the main from the revelatory insights that have come out of the experience and thought of the two communities, science and the Christian Church, within which much of my life has been lived and to both of which I am utterly devoted. Through the latter there has come to me the faith and basic beliefs professed, for example, in the Statement of Faith that we have studied earlier. These insights refer for the most part to God in relation to man, i.e., to God's action in human history and in individual human lives. They do not refer directly to nature, except in so far as it is understood as the ongoing creation of God. By contrast it is the scientific community that has mediated to me the general insights about nature as an orderly and partially predictable cause-and-effect system, as well as the more detailed knowledge of the physical world and its phenomena. Therefore, as I have come to understand and interpret these two bodies of experience, knowledge, faith and belief, they are not fundamentally competitive or inimical. Each complements the other by providing its own unique insights. Certainly both are indispensable to full insight and faith, and to an adequate coping with the difficult problems encountered on the Road.

I for one cannot subscribe to the views of such men as Julian Huxley that science has made it logically impossible to retain traditional religion, if by this is meant the fundamental monotheistic faith of our western culture. On the other hand, it may be that *traditional religion*—conceived as a traditional, religious, cultic system of prescribed symbolic acts, words and ideas, or an organized, institutionalized religious social entity that one must defend at all costs—will have to disappear. Time will tell.*

What is needed first of all is a clearer understanding of the difference between the gods and God, between a faith in a god and

---

* Attention is called to the book *Science Ponders Religion* (X, 2), which contains eighteen essays by as many scientists, all of whom were without doubt moved by genuine concern—probably even ultimate concern—and yet whose attitudes toward traditional religion differ very widely. Especially pertinent in this connection is the essay by Ralph W. Burhoe.[8]

the faith in God, between the faiths and their symbolic expressions, between faith and belief, between immediate and ultimate concerns and commitments. And then what is needed is the courage on the one hand to give up what *is not* essential and meaningful today, and on the other to retain what *is* if properly interpreted. It is my faith that when that is done ultimate faith in God will be seen to support and enrich the more preliminary yet vital faith of science and in science, and that in turn the confidence in and of science will be seen to enrich and strengthen faith in God.

We should note, of course, that, as Professor Niebuhr has pointed out, there is a perpetual tension, both in our culture and in our individual lives, between our loyalty to God and to other gods. Probably in actuality pure monotheism never exists in any culture but for brief interludes. All men are mightily tempted toward idolatry, and give way to it all too often. Hence the tragic features of pluralism. It may be also that this temptation is strong in both the science community and the Church. This is something about which we must be eternally vigilant. And if we are, by God's grace the gates of hell will not prevail.

BIBLIOGRAPHIC REFERENCES

References like that of *Chapter II*, item 5, are to be understood as follows: See book by Whitehead listed under *Chapter I*, as item (1), pages 83, 23, 27, 6.

Chapter I

1. Alfred North Whitehead, *Science and the Modern World*, p. 260, original edition, Macmillan, 1926.
2. Herbert T. Dingle, *The Scientific Adventure*, p. 4, London: Sir Isaac Pitman & Sons, Ltd., 1952.
3. Edmund Husserl, *Die Krisis der Europäischen Wissenschaften und die Transzendentale Phänomenologie*, Haag: Martinus Nijhoff, 1954.
4. H. Richard Niebuhr, *The Meaning of Revelation*, p. 18, Macmillan, 1946.

Chapter II

1. See A. L. Sebaly, ed., *Teacher Education and Religion*, published by The American Association of Colleges for Teacher Education, Washington, D.C., 1959. In chapter entitled "Teaching Reciprocal Relations Between Natural Science and Religion," I have developed somewhat systematically the idea that science exists in at least six recognizably different modes.
2. Martin Buber, *I and Thou*, first printing translated from the German, Edinburgh: T. & T. Clark, 1937. Second edition, Scribners, 1958.
3. Paul Tillich, *The Courage To Be*, p. 186, Yale University Press, 1952.
4. H. Richard Niebuhr, *Radical Monotheism and Western Culture*, Harper, 1960.
5. Whitehead, I (1), pp. 83, 23, 27, 6.
6. The difference between "primal" and "radical" faith has been set forth with great cogency by Clyde A. Holbrook, *Faith and Community*, Harper, 1959.
7. In common discourse faith has many meanings. The Oxford Dic-

tionary recognizes thirteen usages. For a discussion of the two most common in religious language see John Hick, *Faith and Knowledge,* p. xi, Cornell University Press, 1957.

8. George W. Forell, *The Protestant Faith,* p. 312, Prentice-Hall, 1960.

Chapter III

1. Harold K. Schilling, "A Human Enterprise," *Science,* June 6, 1958. Reprinted by permission.
2. P. W. Bridgman, *Yale Review,* XXXIV (1945), p. 444.
3. F. S. C. Northrop, *The Logic of the Sciences and Humanities,* p. viii, Macmillan, 1947.
4. P. W. Bridgman, *Reflections of a Physicist,* p. 370, Philosophical Library, 1950. It is interesting to note that in this context Bridgman uses somewhat different, if not more cogent or colorful, language as follows: "I like to say that there is no scientific method as such, but that the most vital feature of the scientist's procedure has been merely to do his *utmost* with his mind, no holds barred" (italics mine).
5. *Harvard Case Histories of Experimental Science,* ed., James B. Conant, Harvard University Press.
   James B. Conant, *On Understanding Science,* Yale University Press.
   W. I. B. Beveridge, *The Art of Scientific Investigation,* William Heinemann, Ltd., London, third edition, 1957.
   C. P. Snow, *The Search,* Scribners, 1958. Also a Signet Book.
   Morton Thompson, *The Cry and the Covenant,* Signet Book.
6. N. R. Hanson, *Patterns of Discovery,* Cambridge University Press, 1958.
7. Philipp Frank, "Contemporary Science and the Contemporary World View," *Daedalus,* Winter, 1958, p. 65.
8. Michael Polanyi, *Science, Faith and Society,* p. 20, Oxford University Press, 1954. See also his monumental work, *Personal Knowledge,* London: Routledge and Kegan Paul, Ltd., 1958.
9. James K. Senior, "The Vernacular of the Laboratory," *Philosophy of Science,* Vol. 25 (July, 1958), No. 2.
10. *Ibid.,* p. 166.
11. Another suggestive term used by Senior, *ibid.,* p. 164.
12. Niebuhr, I (4).
    John Baillie, *The Idea of Revelation in Recent Thought,* Columbia University Press, 1956.

John L. McKenzie, *The Two-Edged Sword: An Interpretation of the Old Testament*, Bruce, 1956.

13. Daniel Day Williams, *God's Grace and Man's Hope*, p. 50, Harper, 1949.

Chapter IV

1. The term "intersubjective testability" seems to have been suggested first by Herbert Feigl in his essay, "The Scientific Outlook: Naturalism and Humanism," in *American Quarterly*, I (1949).
2. Schilling, III (1), p. 1324.
3. Such an analysis has been reported in a most interesting book by Derek J. de Solla Price, *Science Since Babylon*, Yale University Press, 1961.
4. The communal aspects of science and Christianity have been set forth by William G. Pollard in *Physicist and Christian*, Seabury Press, 1961.
5. Two books considering problems arising out of dual communal loyalties are: Ian G. Barbour, *Christianity and the Scientist*, Association Press, 1960; and C. A. Coulson, *Science, Technology and the Christian*, Abingdon Press, 1960.
6. A well-known example is offered by D. C. Mackintosh, *Theology As An Empirical Science*, Macmillan, 1940.

Chapter V

1. Andrew D. White, *A History of the Warfare of Science with Theology in Christendom*, first published in two volumes in 1895, but recently republished in one by George Braziller, New York, 1955.
2. Richard S. Westfall, *Science and Religion in Seventeenth-Century England*, Yale University Press, 1958.
   John Dillenberger, *Protestant Thought and Natural Science*, Doubleday & Company, 1960.
3. Roger Hazelton, *New Accents in Contemporory Theology*, Harper, 1960.
   William A. Spurrier, *Guide to the Christian Faith*, Scribners, 1952.
   For an excellent, annotated bibliography see Walter M. Horton, *Christian Theology: An Ecumenical Approach*, Harper, 1958.
   Gustav Aulén, *The Faith of the Christian Church* (translation), Muhlenberg Press, 1948.

4. Fernand Renoirte, *Cosmology: Elements of a Critique of the Sciences and of Cosmology*, p. 15, Joseph F. Wagner, Inc., 1950. This book presents a remarkably lucid and cogent analysis of the empirical and theoretical aspects of the subject of chemical reactions.

5. Edited by W. R. Matthews and Gordon Rupp, published by Nisbet & Co., Ltd., London. Most of its volumes have been reprinted many times, indicating their great significance and perennial timeliness.

6. For an able analysis of his writings, see Gordon Harland, *The Thought of Reinhold Niebuhr*, pp. vii, viii, Oxford University Press, 1960.

7. Paul Tillich, *Systematic Theology*, Vol. I, p. 8, University of Chicago Press, 1953.

8. Walter M. Horton, *Christian Theology: An Ecumenical Approach*, Harper, 1958.

Chapter VI

1. Mark Graubard, *Astrology and Alchemy, Two Fossil Sciences*, Philosophical Library, 1953.

2. For first-hand accounts of the determinations of the speed of light by Roemer, Bradley and others, see William F. Magie, *A Source Book in Physics*, McGraw-Hill, 1935.

   For a lucid introductory textook account, see Duncan and Starling, *Textbook of Physics*, Chapter 51, Macmillan, 1927.

3. Stephen Toulmin in his *The Philosophy of Science* (Hutchinson's University Library, Hutchinson House, 1953) has provided an excellent analysis of the physicist's ways of thinking with respect to the concept of *the velocity of light*.

4. R. A. Millikan, *Electrons, Protons, Photons, Neutrons and Cosmic Rays*, The University of Chicago Press, 1935.

5. A first-hand account of this experiment may be found in Magie, VI (2). For its theoretical significance, see Albert Einstein, *Relativity*, Peter Smith, 1931. (Probably this little book by Einstein himself is the best "popular" interpretation of his relativity theories.)

   Lincoln Barnett, *The Universe and Dr. Einstein*, A Mentor Book, 1953.

6. Ludwig Fleck, *Entstehung und Entwicklung einer Wissenschaftlichen Tatsache, Einführung in die Lehre vom Denkstil und Denkkollektiv*, Bruno Schwabe & Co., Basel, 1935.

Chapter VII

1. For these apt terms I am indebted to Philip Wheelwright, *The Burning Fountain: A Study in the Language of Symbolism,* Indiana University Press, 1954.
2. P. Schaff, *Creeds of Christendom,* 3 vols., Harper, 1905.
3. J. F. Bethune-Baker, *Introduction to the Early History of Christian Doctrine,* London: Methuen & Co., 1903.
4. Tillich, V (7), p. 108.
5. Concerning the "Word of God," see Hazelton, V (3), Chapter III.
6. For excellent expositions of contemporary insights concerning the nature of the Bible, see Bernhard W. Anderson, *Rediscovering the Bible,* Association Press, 1959.
   Abraham Joshua Heschel, *God in Search of Man,* Farrar, Straus & Cudahy, 1955.
7. Alfred North Whitehead, *Religion in the Making,* p. 58, Macmillan, 1926.
8. Beveridge, III (5).
9. Daniel Day Williams, *What Present-Day Theologians Are Thinking,* Chapter I, Harper, 1952.

Chapter VIII

1. Williams, III (13), p. 41.
2. F. S. C. Northrop, *The Meeting of East and West,* Macmillan, 1946.
3. Philipp Frank, *Philosophy of Science,* Prentice-Hall, 1957. Hanson, III (6).
   Henry Margenau, *The Nature of Physical Reality,* McGraw-Hill, 1950.
   Ernest Nagel, *The Structure of Science,* Harcourt, Brace, 1961. Toulmin, VI (3).
4. See the collection of essays on this subject in Philipp Frank, ed., *The Validation of Scientific Theories,* Beacon Press, 1957.
5. H. Poincaré, *Science and Hypothesis,* English translation republished by Dover, 1952.
6. To help people to develop a feel for the possibility of different kinds of geometry Poincaré constructed an imaginary world with unusual geometric properties that do not conform to the Euclidian ones. This is sometimes called the Poincaré world. For lucid discussions of it that are not beyond the competence of the ordinary

reader, see John Wesley Young, *Lectures on Fundamental Concepts of Algebra and Geometry*, Macmillan, 1917; Hassler and Smith, *The Teaching of Secondary Mathematics*, Chapter V ("Non-Euclidian Geometry"), Macmillan, 1930; Richard Courant and Herbert Robbins, *What Is Mathematics?*, Oxford University Press, 1953. The general subject of non-Euclidian geometries is, of course, also pertinent here. See these same authors.

Chapter IX

1. Evelyn Underhill, *Worship*, London: Nisbet & Co., 1951.
   Rudolf Otto, *The Idea of the Holy*, Oxford University Press, 1952.
   Friedrich Heiler, *Prayer*, Oxford University Press, 1933.
2. See, e.g., Mircea Eliade, *The Sacred and the Profane: The Nature of Religion*, Harcourt, Brace, 1959.
3. John Knox, *Criticism and Faith*, Abingdon-Cokesbury Press, 1952.
4. John Dillenberger, *God Hidden and Revealed*, Muhlenberg Press, 1953.
5. *Doctrine in the Church of England*, published in London by the Society for Promoting Christian Knowledge, 1938, pp. 60 and 61 (New York: The Macmillan Co.).
6. *Ibid.*, p. 62.
7. *Ibid.*, p. 79.
8. *Ibid.*, pp. 163 and 164.
9. For a lucid study of these two miracles, as well as miracles in general, see Anderson, VII (6), Chapters 3, 8, 9.
10. The following three books discuss miracles from different points of view in the light of modern science: Karl Heim, *The Transformation of the Scientific World View*, Harper, 1953; C. S. Lewis, *Miracles*, Macmillan, 1947; William G. Pollard, *Chance and Providence*, Scribners, 1958.
11. Niebuhr, I (4), pp. 138–140.

Chapter X

1. Margenau, VIII (3); also *Open Vistas*, Yale University Press, 1961.
2. See Margenau's chapter, "Truth in Science and Religion," in *Science Ponders Religion*, Harlow Shapley, ed., Appleton-Century, 1960.
3. Ernst Mach, *Science of Mechanics*, p. 364, Open Court Publishing Co., 1919; also his Chapter IV, Section 11: "Theological, Ani-

mistic and Mystical Points of View in Mechanics," especially p. 454, "The theological kernel of the principle of least action."

4. Dillenberger, V (2), p. 122; Edwin A. Burtt, *The Metaphysical Foundations of Modern Physical Science,* Harcourt, Brace, 1927. How common this practice was can be seen by consulting such works as John C. Greene, *The Death of Adam,* Iowa State University Press, 1959; and Charles C. Gillispie, *Genesis and Geology,* Harper, 1959 (now Harper Torchbook).

5. Frank, VIII (4).

6. Joseph Needham, *Science and Civilization in China,* Vol. 2, Cambridge University Press, 1956.

7. Herbert Butterfield, *The Origins of Modern Science,* p. 104, London: G. Bell and Sons, Ltd., 1951.

8. Whitehead, I (1), p. 17. The inadequacy of this kind of argument is discussed by Robert S. Cohen in an essay entitled "Alternative Interpretations of the History of Science," and in Frank, VIII (4).

9. Dillenberger, V (2), pp. 251, 290, 292.

10. Harold K. Schilling, *Concerning the Nature of Science and Religion: A Study of Presuppositions,* a lecture published by the School of Religion, The State University of Iowa, 1958.

11. In some of the standard books on the philosophy of science; also in others such as E. F. Caldin, *The Power and Limits of Science,* London: Chapman and Hall, 1949; C. A. Coulson, *Science and Christian Belief,* University of North Carolina Press, 1955; R. H. Dotterer, *Postulates and Implications,* Philosophical Library, 1955.

12. Lucien Price, *Dialogues of Alfred North Whitehead,* Little, Brown, 1954.

13. Presuppositions of this negative type, especially as they may have a bearing on religious thought, have been considered at length by C. D. Broad in his *Religion, Philosophy and Psychical Research,* London: Routledge & Kegan Paul, 1953.

Chapter XI

1. Harold K. Schilling, "On Relating Science and Religion," *The Christian Scholar,* XLI (September, 1958), No. 3, p. 392.

2. J. Robert Oppenheimer, "The Growth of Science and the Structure of Culture," *Daedalus,* Winter 1958, pp. 75, 76.

3. J. Robert Oppenheimer, *Science and the Common Understanding,* Simon and Schuster, 1954.

4. John A. Mackay, *A Preface to Christian Theology*, p. 30, Macmillan, 1941.
5. *Ibid.*
6. Ephesians 6:12.
7. Stephen Toulmin, "Scientific Theories and Scientific Myths," in *Metaphysical Beliefs*, Macintyre, ed., London: SCM Press Ltd., 1957.
8. Regarding contemporary usages of the word "myth," see Susanne K. Langer, *Philosophy in a New Key*, Scribners, 1955 (also published as Mentor Book); Ernst Cassirer, *Language and Myth*, Dover Publications, 1953. With respect to religious discourse, see many references to myth in Tillich, V (7), and Bernard E. Meland, *Faith and Culture*, Oxford University Press, 1953.
9. Meland, XI (8), p. 20.
10. B. Davie Napier, *From Faith to Faith: Essays on Old Testament Literature*, Harper, 1955.
11. Wheelwright, VII (1), Chapter I.
12. Toulmin, XI (7).
13. Pierre Teilhard de Chardin, *The Phenomenon of Man*, Harper, 1959 (also a Harper Torchbook).
14. Henri Bergson, *Creative Evolution*, The Modern Library, 1944.
    Julian Huxley, *Evolution in Action*, Harper, 1953.
    Edmund W. Sinnott, *The Biology of the Spirit*, Viking Press, 1955; *Matter, Mind and Man*, Harper, 1957.
15. John Baillie, *The Belief in Progress*, Scribners, 1951.
16. Hazelton, V (3), pp. 43–47.
17. Niebuhr, II (4), p. 11.
18. See "Postscript," in Max Born, *The Restless Universe*, Dover Publications, 1951, for an utterly frank portrayal of this point of view that comes close to utter despair—though it does hold out some hope.
19. George Orwell, *1984*, Harcourt, Brace, 1949; published as Signet Book, 1952.
    Aldous Huxley, *Brave New World*, Doubleday, 1932; Bantam Books, 1953. *Brave New World Revisited*, Harper, 1958; Bantam Books, 1960.

Chapter XII

1. Huston Smith, *The Religions of Mankind*, Harper, 1958, Mentor Books, 1959.
2. Needham, X (6).

3. Price, IV (3).
4. O. Neugebauer, *The Exact Sciences in Antiquity,* Brown University Press, second edition, 1957.
5. Niebuhr, I (4), p. 32.
6. Smith, XII (1), pp. 2, 313.
7. Niebuhr, II (4), pp. 38, 32.
8. Ralph W. Burhoe, "Salvation in the Twentieth Century," in Shapley, X (2).

INDEX

INDEX

Aberration, 32, 244f.
Abraham, 46, 60, 162
Abstraction, 188
Analogy(ies), 13, 41, 66
Anderson, Bernhard W., 253f.
Applications, *see* Transformation
Apprehension, 146, 172, 176
A-priori, 85f., 101, 166, 187, 199
Archimedes, 132
Aristotle, 96, 199, 203
Art(s), 12, 66, 77, 194f.
Astrology, 93f.
Astronomy, 74, 100, 187, 214, 239
Atheist, 63f.
Atomic age, 220
Attitude(s), 6ff.
Aulén, Gustav, 133, 251
Authority, authoritarian, 4, 16, 48, 136f., 215

Baillie, John, 4, 133, 250, 256
Barbour, Ian, 251
Barnett, Lincoln, 252
Barth, Karl, 16, 133
Being, 18, 24, 26, 246
Belief, believe, 5, 9f., 25ff., 29f., 68, 109f., 112f., 116–119, 124f., 157, 172, 176, 205, 225, 234f.
Berdyaev, N., 133
Bergson, Henri, 227, 256
Bethune-Baker, J. F., 253
Beveridge, W. I. B., 38, 250, 253

Bible, 5, 23, 79, 116, 118, 129, 183, 187, 225
Biology, biologist, 3, 12, 40, 56, 119, 194f., 220, 240
Bohr atom, 94, 119
Born, Max, 233, 256
Bradley, 100, 252
Bridgman, P. W., 36 ff., 250
Broad, C. D., 255
Brunner, Emil, 133
Buber, Martin, 22, 249
Bultmann, Rudolf, 133
Burhoe, Ralph W., 247n., 257
Burtt, Edwin A., 255
Butterfield, Herbert, 202, 255

Caldin, E. F., 255
Calvin, 133
Cassirer, Ernst, 256
Catholic, 46, 83
Cause and effect, 23, 30, 101, 130, 179f., 189, 224, 227, 247
Certainty, 11, 88, 90, 92, 94, 106–109, 176, 192
C-field, 187f., 191, 194ff., 215
Chemistry, chemist, 40, 43, 55f., 71–74, 86, 137, 195, 197
China, 202, 243
Christ, 16, 30, 47, 58, 61, 63, 78ff., 117, 119, 127f., 134, 164ff., 173, 178f., 228, 241; -event as miracle, 178; is meaning, 164; presence in communion, 170

261